end

1   Since the introduction of the NHS reforms, the strengths and the pitfalls of the health services in England and Wales have become the focus of wide public interest and debate as never before. This is an inevitable result of the public scrutiny that attends an institution that the nation holds sacred. It reflects shifts in societal patterns and styles. It is also the result of legislative initiatives that have directly sought to engage the public – in the form of *client, customer,* or *consumer* of services – in the way services are planned and delivered; a process that fits the business and market-orientated paradigms of the reformed service.

2   The representation of health service *clients* is provided for in many forms. Through the Patient's Charter, all members of the public – that is, all potential and actual *clients* or *users* of services – have guidelines posing the nature and delivery of health services that they can expect.

3   Other legislation, stemming from the Griffiths Report, *Community Care: Agenda for Action* (1988), primarily the *NHS and Community Care Act 1990* and, more recently, the *Carers (Recognition and Services) Act 1995,* all encourage and promote the active engagement of the public in all aspects of commissioning, planning, delivering and evaluating health services. Added to this, in the realm particularly of mental health services, the Health of the Nation strategic initiative has addressed mental illness as a target area.

4   While the effects of the most recent legislation cannot be assessed yet, developments in the way *carers* and *users* (the two most vital sectors of the health services consumer population) play a part in the process of service developments, have been well highlighted since the reforms.

5   I use the term highlighted rather than any more approbatory notion such as increased or improved, because, whatever the political will, and however it is supported by legislation, the objective of giving users and carers an effective voice in all aspects of the health services that are commissioned and delivered on their behalf, cannot be achieved overnight. There are many tensions at the interfaces between users and carers and the wide range of professional people who manage and deliver health services in hospital and in the community. Some of these tensions appear to be attitudinal, in circumstances, for example, in which a professional person sits happily alongside a carer or user of services, hears what they have to say about their needs, receives their feedback and suggestions about services, and then appears to ignore them, perhaps because the professional is convinced he or she knows better or that his or her opinions have overriding value. Conceptually at least, such a tension should not be a problem and should be gradually reduced as professionals get used to the idea that user and carer representation is an advantageous opportunity. Already professionals are taught to listen and take note, now they will need to assess the fine line between what a user and carer *need* and what they appear to *wish.* Such an assessment cannot be performed by professionals on their own and requires continuing dialogue between users, carers and professionals. A tension that parallels this one is the deep distaste that users and carers have for being patronised.

6   Another complication is that users and carers are not a homogeneous group. Sometimes, tensions may exist between them. Users often have different agendas for their care, compared with the agendas of those who care for them. Carers have to be considered as a separate entity from users, particularly as concerns the issue of supporting them in their own vital provision of services to users.

7   Moreover, what do we consider an effective voice for users and carers to be, in terms of their representation within the planning and delivery of health services? If it is voice that signifies taking full part in the way services are organised and delivered, do users and carers have equal responsibility if services that they participate in planning fail? There are many nice questions of this kind addressed in this report, and by drawing attention to them, we are drawing attention to considerations that need to be made across commissioning, purchasing and providing elements of the statutory services much as within leading voluntary agencies.

8   As this report explains, there are critically important reasons for including the constructive influence of users and carers in the development of services. They are particularly important in the provision of mental health services, which continue – hopefully to a lessening extent – to carry the unwarranted labels of taboo and stigma.

9   Clearly, what we have to beware of, following the synthesis of evidence put before us in the report that follows, is the development of a health service that pays tokenistic heed to users and carers because that is what it is supposed to do. The complexities of involving users and carers in every aspect of the services that are rendered on their behalf make it very difficult to define and to allocate specific types of user and carer input in every different type of service component. But these complexities challenge the process and mechanisms of involvement, not the value of involvement itself, which is unquestionable.

10   From the vantage point of the NHS Health Advisory Service (HAS), the involvement of users and carers has been thoroughly instrumental in the entire range of work that has been carried out under my directorship since 1992. During this time we have carried out a number of major thematic reviews, each of which has followed a stratagem of gaining first-hand experience from a number of health service and local authority commissioners, providers, non-statutory services and users and carers themselves. In one such review, *A Place in Mind* (HMSO, 1995d), which concerned mental health service provision for homeless mentally ill people, the voice of users is very strongly represented. But all these thematic reviews, as well as the local review reports and publications giving account of specialist reviews, emphasise the needs of users and carers, often pinpointing where their representation in service provision is lacking, but always soliciting their views.

11   In the report that follows, we outline the challenges to user and carer participation and recommend that they are addressed. This is not because we are extolling some fashionable democratisation of the health services, but because it is evident that we will best improve the provision of health services by focusing closely on what is needed most, as learned from those most in need.

12   Although this report has been written by mental health professionals and, then, edited for publication by the HAS, its origin lies in the inspiration of the Steering Committee (see Annex). Each of its members has given selflessly of their valuable experience and each has played a vital role in shaping the direction and content of the review. I am most grateful to all these people for their commitment and hard work. I hope that this report does, in some measure, take account of the enormous influence that they have had on the work of the NHS Health Advisory Service during the last five years.

Richard Williams

Director

NHS Health Advisory Service

September 1996

CHAPTER 2

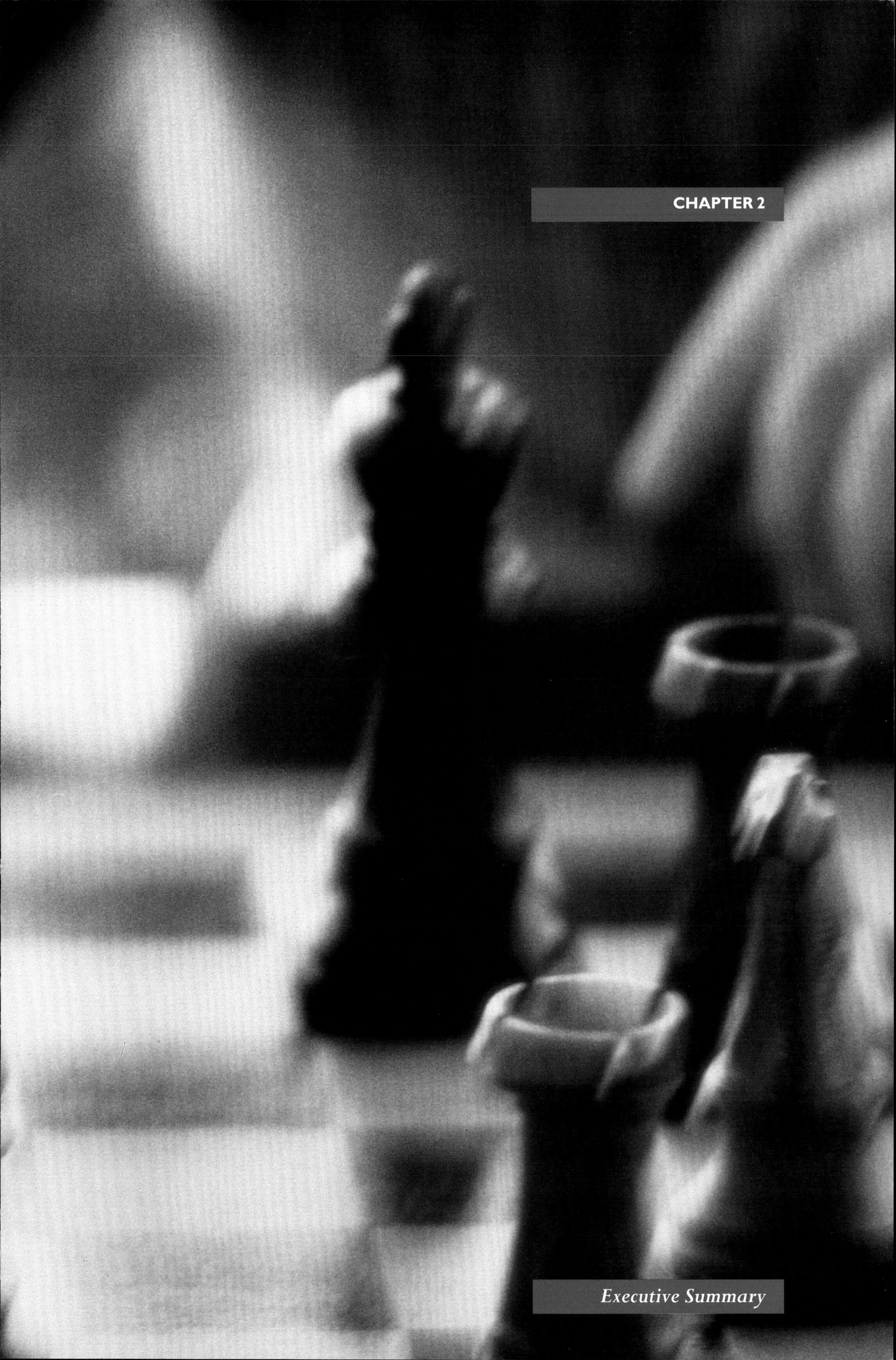

Executive Summary

INTRODUCTION

13   This review is based on:

- thematic reviews conducted by the NHS Health Advisory Service (HAS);

- reports and site visits prepared and conducted at the instigation of the HAS in the period 1994-96;

- surveys, site visits and analyses of the literature conducted for the HAS for this review; as well as on

- selected documentation on community care planning.

It focuses on adults who utilise mental health services (users) and their adult carers. It does not address specifically the needs or involvement of young people, elderly people or people within the ethnic minorities.

THE EFFECTS OF RECENT LEGISLATION

14   To date, it would appear that the empowerment of users and carers, that was expected to follow the implementation of the *NHS and Community Care Act 1990,* has been slow and inconsistent in its development. Since the *Carers (Recognition and Services) Act 1995* was only introduced on 1 April 1996, it is too early to say what effect this legislation will have.

15   The implementation of the care programme approach (CPA) in England has been slow and uneven, and carers' needs are not being assessed as routinely as users' needs.

16   Financial assessments for services such as respite or residential care, domiciliary support or spot purchasing often include an assessment of carers' incomes, or the joint income of carers and users. Opinion provided to the HAS is that this is probably unlawful.

THE ROLE OF USERS AND CARERS IN SERVICE PLANNING AND DELIVERY

17   While the status of users and carers as partners in the businesses of commissioning and providing care is developing rapidly, it remains far from established in many parts of the country.

18   The purposes of involving users and carers in planning and delivering services should be clarified by health and local authorities, trusts and all other relevant services. Participation can be seen as an end in itself, providing a personally therapeutic experience, group identity and collective empowerment. For some, the role is that of ensuring the better targeting and responsiveness of services provided for identified individuals. For others, participation is a means towards corporate, rather than personal, goals, such as structural changes in services, or improved quality of life for the users of mental health services and the population of carers.

19   A focus on users and carers should permeate strategic planning, operational policies and the practical ways in which services are provided.

20   The credibility of commissioners and purchasers is enhanced by the involvement and influence of users and carers in planning, quality monitoring and development and performance management. These give authenticity to the services themselves, and integrity to auditing processes.

21   This report considers three typologies for understanding the level and aims of user and carer roles in mental health services. It is hoped that these will prove helpful to users, carers, commissioners, providers and individual professionals in considering and discussing and thereby, making progress in the wide arena of user and carer involvement.

SOURCES OF CONFLICT

22   User/consumer choice *(wishes)* may conflict with agency criteria for delivering the services that they consider to be essential *(needs)*.

23   In some respects, modern market principles may stand in contradiction to traditional welfare principles.

24   Users and carers are different groups of people. Their needs and wishes are different and, on occasions, may be contradictory.

25   Recent shifts in service culture, such as the promotion of client independence and self-reliance, could deny to clients with enduring needs their right to proper dependency on services. That is unless care is exercised through the active involvement of users and carers in both service commissioning and delivery and both processes are conducted in open awareness of the needs of people with enduring problems that reduce their abilities to act as their own advocates.

26   On the other hand, balanced user and carer representation is not easy to achieve. Even with appropriate resourcing, there is the challenge posed by creating so-called professional user or carer representatives and the risk that they may exert disproportionate influence or distorted views on planning bodies.

THE WAY FORWARD

27   A particular issue concerns resourcing the involvement of users and carers. Among its recommendations as to the way forward, this review suggests options for resolving the resource challenges. These include:

- employment of salaried user-/carer-involvement workers to collect, collate and interpret data on opinions, wishes and needs or to stimulate or co-ordinate actions by groups of users or carers;

- creation of user and carer initiative grants;

- training and time for users and carers to develop knowledge and skills;

- mainstream funding from health and local authorities incorporated within strategic healthcare plans. Funding of this kind is needed to cover facilities (bases, office-space, administrative and secretarial support), transport, personal expenses, setting up network registers and helplines, and the costs to carers of replacements to substitute for them;

- the wider use of professional advocates to accompany or represent users and carers at meetings relating to forward planning and service delivery.

The Background

CHAPTER 3

Background Perspectives

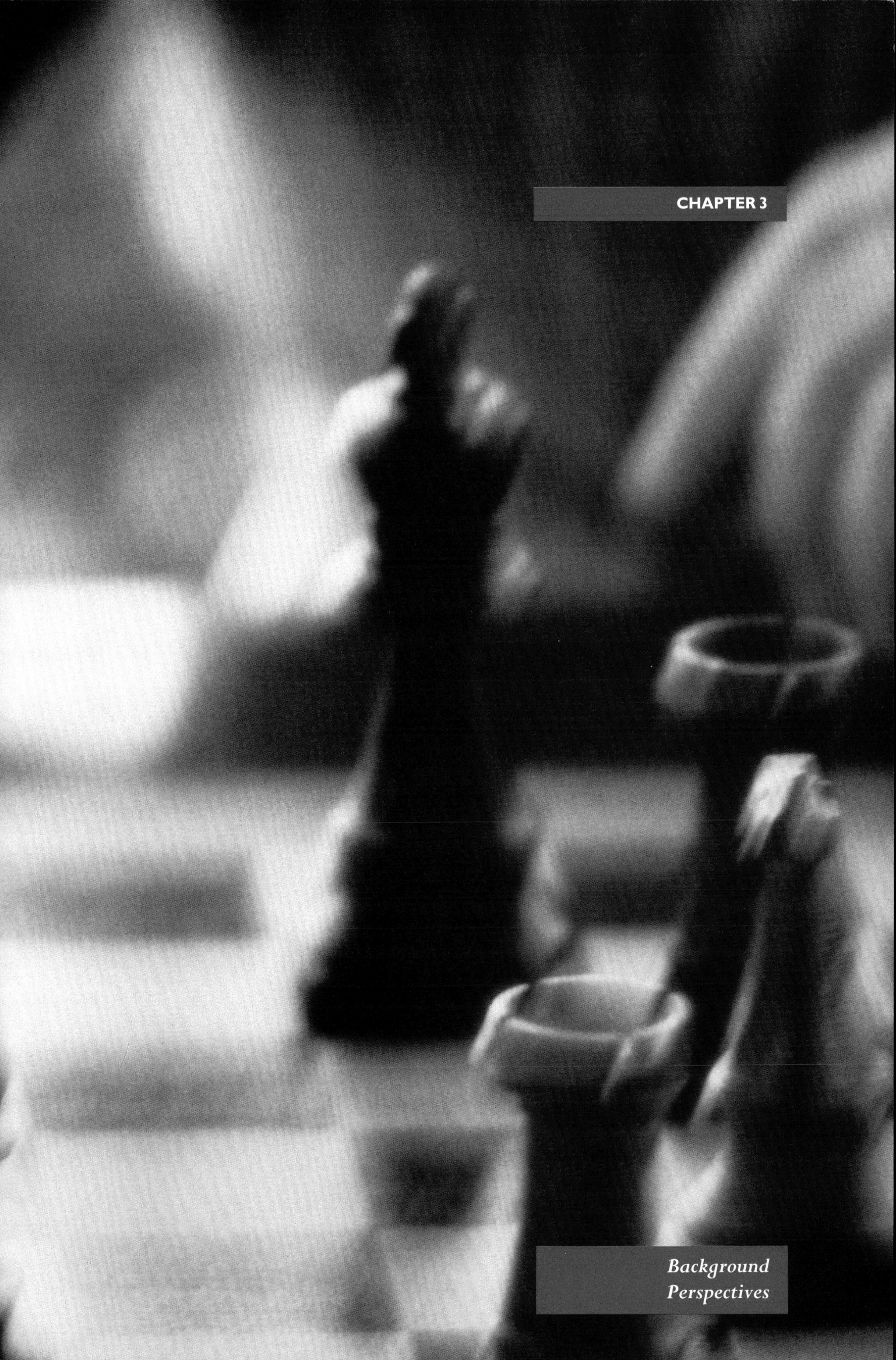

INTRODUCTION

28   One of the significant shifts in the style of public services that has occurred in the last decade is that of an increased focus on the relationships between the consumers of those services and the employees who staff them. The consumers are variously styled as *patients, clients, customers or users*, depending on the orientation and training of the staff, the nature of the service and the preference of the consumers.

29   The shift in emphasis that has resulted is summarised in Table 1 (Drinkwater, 1995).

Table 1

Turning Principles into Practice		
Issue	**Standard Practice**	**Good Practice**
Perspective	Professional	A balance of patient, carer and professional
Aims and objectives	Assumed	Specified
Focus	Throughput of people, or cases	Effective processes and systems
Quality	Appeals to professional standards	Incorporates internally generated continuous quality improvements alongside professional standards
Training	Profession specific	A balance of team-based and profession specific training

30   This review considers the increasing role and views of users and their carers and their participation in the design and delivery of services. The HAS could have considered the whole range of services within its remit in this regard. However, for preference, the focus chosen in this review is on the users of mental health services and their carers. This reflects the particularly rapid developments in the involvement of users and carers in mental health services over the last five to ten years. The review begins by summarising some of the historical, policy and other background matters that give the review its context.

PERSPECTIVES

The Reforms of the NHS and Community Care

31   This review has been conducted against the background of considerable changes in legislation and service provision stemming, notably, from the Griffiths Report, *Community Care: Agenda for Action* (1988), which recognised consumerism as a factor in impending welfare reforms; and the *NHS and Community Care Act 1990*, which placed some emphasis on the empowerment of users and carers. In addition, the government has sought to provide a new impetus towards addressing the needs of carers through the introduction of the *Carers (Recognition and Services) Act 1995*. It is still too early to determine what effect this may have.

Policy Developments

32   While the carers' movement in the United Kingdom can be regarded as having begun in the 1960s with Mary Webster's *Single Women and their Dependents* alliance, the users' movement has a more recent history. The latter has been stimulated particularly by the relocation of long-stay patients from older psychiatric hospitals, with added momentum from the *Health of the Nation* strategic initiative in England and the *Patient's Charter* initiatives in England and Wales. Mental illness is one of this initiative's key areas. In 1989, Wales adopted a specific mental health strategy, entitled *Mental Illness Services – A Strategy for Wales*.

33   Another specific central government influence has been the instigation of the care programme approach in England, which requires statutory services to be more responsive to the preferences and opinions of users and carers. These changes in service provision have borrowed from North American models of case and care management. As well as supporting a de-professionalised class of workers, American practices have brought in users as advocates and co-workers, at operational levels.

34   In line with *Health of the Nation* initiatives in England, and the Welsh mental health strategy, there is greater focus on quality of life and needs-based services, and, for some users, these replace former maintenance models of care. Hence, assessment and evaluation processes now give higher priority to the views of users and, to a lesser degree, to those of carers.

35   User and carer groups are a developing phenomenon. User groups are now common adjuncts to hospital services, but do not yet sufficiently permeate strategic planning, commissioning, purchasing and service delivery infrastructures. Most user and carer groups aim to ensure that civil liberties and human rights are not incidental considerations as mental health services are re-shaped. Nationally, these groups include MIND, the Afro-Caribbean Mental Health Association, the Carers National Association, and a range of other user-informed voluntary sector organisations. Government-supported equivalents have included the Community Care Support Force and the Mental Health Task Force. In Wales, the strategic document *Mental Illness Services – A Strategy for Wales* has facilitated user involvement, including the funding of a user-involvement development worker.

36   One of the central planks of government policy has been the separation of purchasers and providers within local authority social services departments and between health authorities, GP fundholders and NHS trusts. Only GP fundholders retain the responsibilities for both purchasing and providing services. This separation of functions between purchasers and providers had the objective of ensuring that the care purchased and provided met the needs of the local population in the most cost-effective way, with contracts being used to formalise relationships between the funding and service delivery bodies in respect of service strategic directions and the volumes and quality of services provided. This shift in service planning and delivery has brought its own tensions and paradoxes. For instance, if the customer is key, then he or she should be heard at the highest strategic level of this business-oreintated hierachy.

37   Some of the titles in current use highlight the dilemmas inherent in a business-orientated vision of community care. *User* denotes a recipient of services – willingly or otherwise. *Consumer*, with its connotations of freer choice, is a difficult notion to apply to formally detained patients. *Customer*, with its associated images of supermarket trolleys and checkout tills, is both misleading and demeaning. How much choice, in terms of alternatives to institutional care, do the patients of mental health services have?

38   Stresses in the workplace have led to increasing numbers of the staff of health and welfare services becoming users of the services. This may have unforeseen benefits in reducing the psychological distance between professionals and users, and may stimulate more approaches led from the bottom in the re-organisation of services.

39   Overall, the involvement of users and carers in health service planning and commissioning remains in its infancy, with a number of exceptions. Examples include the user and carer forums in North Wales and in Nottingham. Users and carers should develop their own collective voices. But they will require democratic infrastructures, committee skills, better office bases, administrative support, and greater assertiveness before they can join on equal terms with the managerial and professional members of existing planning groups.

SUMMARY

40   In retrospect, the question that arises is: *"What is the purpose of involving users and carers in planning and delivering services?"* There are several aims to consider:

   •   Service change; if this is the objective of user- and carer-involvement, then non-users should also be involved, for balance;

   •   Improved mental health for some individuals; service change does not in itself guarantee improved mental health;

   •   Improved mental health within the population as a whole; if this is the goal, then any changes which might be evidence of improved mental health in the population need to be vigorously evaluated.

   •   Participation of users and carers; if this is the goal, rather than the means towards a goal, then it needs to be borne in mind that not every user will find the experience helpful.

CHAPTER 4

*The Nature of
the Review*

THE AIMS OF THE REVIEW

41   This report has briefly summarised the main policy and social shifts that have changed relationships between users and their carers and the staff of services. To some, these developments and the changed status of users and carers are long overdue. To others, the changes are more contentious and are seen as marking the changed status of professionals in western society. The spectrum of differing opinions about this changing status is particularly broad. This is reflected in later chapters of this report.

42   For some people, the advances in user and carer status, and the more democratic relationships between them and service employees, still do not go far enough. In the chapter on typologies, the HAS considers two ways of approaching this. Also, it identifies a spectrum of levels of participation by users and carers, and, within that, the so-called *oppositional stance*.

43   Despite diverse opinion in this rapidly changing field, much has been achieved and there is no doubt that increasing influence of users and carers on services is now a firm part of service developments. This review takes into account the pace of changing developments in this field and the experiences of the HAS in visiting services over the last five years. It summarises the current position as a guide for users, carers, commissioners, purchasers, the responsible authorities, providers of services and individual managers and professionals. The intention of this report is not that the HAS should espouse or appear to espouse any one position in the spectrum of levels of participation of users and carers, more that this document should be a source of information and provoke thinking and action locally.

44   The HAS has conducted a review of the literature, and, through its visits, a review of the lessons that have been learned. These are offered in this report as a ready reference and source.

45   The report begins by reviewing the present situation and observations that have arisen in the course of the HAS performing its wider functions. It then provides an analysis of the various roles and positions that users and carers may adopt, endeavours to summarise this in two typologies before considering in more detail, in chapters 10, 11 and 12, the issues relating to certain of these activities in the purchaser-provider system.

TERMINOLOGY

46   Highly specific definitions of key terms such as *user, carer* and *professional* are not necessary for the purposes of this review. Here, *user* is taken to mean anyone who has sought or received help for a mental health problem, a *carer* is a person who provides regular and substantial care for a user, beyond that of occasional help, and a *professional* is a salaried, trained mental health worker or a manager of services who is accountable to an agency or professional body.

47   The processes of commissioning, purchasing and contracting have been usefully described by the HAS (1995b). Commissioning implies a strategically driven process. Purchasing refers to the various technical procedures whereby purchasers secure and monitor the delivery of services by other agencies. Contracting is the component of purchasing by which the nature and level of service provision is agreed.

SOURCE MATERIAL

48   The content of this review has been drawn from documentation on the involvement of users and carers in the recent changes to community care services, especially the planning process. These include papers, studies and reviews that have been commissioned by a variety of agencies, including the HAS. Each has been researched independently.

49   Further sources have included HAS reviews and reports, as well as meetings with users conducted in several sites, such as Gwynedd, South Glamorgan, Macclesfield, Newcastle, London and Nottingham, by personnel seconded to the HAS for the purpose. Additional sources are reports and articles found in specialist carer and user magazines and reports and other periodicals.

50   The papers, reports and other supporting documentation used in preparing this review are recorded in chapter 14 (Bibliography and References). The documents referred to in chapter 3 are grouped together in the first part of that chapter. Quotations from users or the various texts have been used sparingly, and the sources have not been identified, to ensure anonymity.

THE SIGNIFICANCE OF INVOLVING USERS AND CARERS

51   Users and carers have been central to the discussions and documentation which have informed this review. This is consistent with the core theme of the review itself, which aims to reflect how instrumental users and carers are currently, in influencing policy at the highest level, and practice at an operational level. The review concludes with some pointers on how this influence might develop in the immediate future.

52   The HAS hopes that its analysis of the present position and roles of users and carers in mental healthcare services will prove helpful. By providing a snapshot of the current position of developments and an accumulation of lessons learned, it may help to determine appropriate service developments in this critically important area.

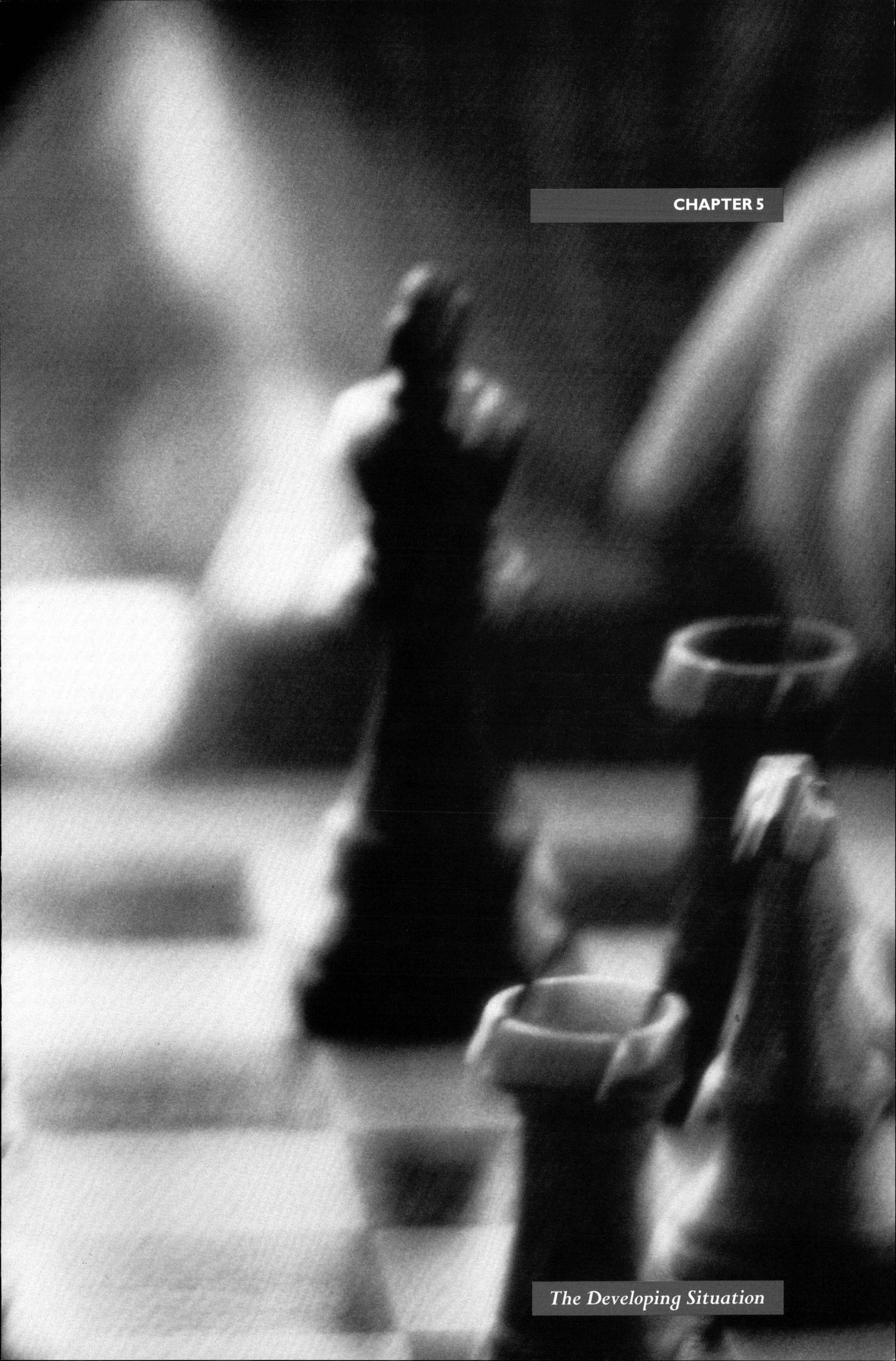

CHAPTER 5

The Developing Situation

ISSUES AND DILEMMAS – EVIDENCE EMERGING FROM COMPARATIVE STUDIES

53   Overall, the present state of user and carer involvement in the commissioning and delivery of mental health services is not clear. It is apparent, however, that some parts of England and Wales have better developed and integrated user and carer representation in their planning, quality management and service delivery processes than others. This may reflect demographic features such as a stable local population, strongly-motivated individuals, and a good history of incorporation of users and carers in services.

54   But the explanations of the HAS indicate that, alongside examples of good practice, there remain many dilemmas and difficulties inherent in involving users or carers. These can best be represented as the series of tensions that are listed here. Each is annotated to give, briefly, a flavour of the matters that are in tension. At its close, this chapter highlights the issues stemming from the questions as how to best resource and support users and carers.

Common Tensions

The User's Wishes versus His/Her Needs

55   A user may know what he or she wants and how he or she feels, but this may not necessarily be considered by others to be in his or her best interests. Thus, the wishes and needs of individuals, as defined here, are not necessarily synonymous. Related to this is the issue of client self-determination and civil rights versus professional judgement and the duty of workers to provide appropriate care.

Agency versus User Definitions of Need

56   This tension is similar to the one cited above in respect of individuals but, in this instance, refers to the conceptions of need at organisational, corporate and population levels. Service agencies face many dilemmas. The dilemma that arises when attempting to differentiate between *needs* and *wishes* of individuals is replicated when endeavouring to balance these issues for populations or client groups in respect of service strategy development.

57   Research and anecdotal user opinion clearly indicate that the quality of users' lives is dependent on basic needs (accommodation, money, food, security) being met but also on more than this. Higher orders of personal experience include whether users are able to exercise personal choice in securing services that meet the expression of their wishes (preferences), and not, solely, their needs (essentials). Hence, a problem for purchasers and providers is how to prioritise and manage budgets to ensure essential needs are met, but leaving leeway for funding those additions to basic needs which may improve material living standards and subjective well-being. There is a place for users, carers, commissioners and providers to work together to determine these priorities.

Market Principles versus Human Service Principles

58   The user and carer movements are developing in parallel to other government initiatives, for example the *Citizen's Charter* and the *Patient's Charter*, which direct all organisations, public and private, to take account of the views of the recipients of their services. All citizens, in every walk of life, are being encouraged to feel empowered and to challenge the views of service providers.

59   The HAS supports the notion that everyone should have the right to challenge the service they are being offered. Nonetheless, it also recognises that this can produce difficulties. Increasingly, nationally and locally, user and carer movements are themselves service providers. When this is the case, two potentially contentious issues come to the fore: should the provider of one service sit on the board/executive committee of another service; and will users and carers feel able to challenge the provider of a service which, theoretically, represents them?

Medical and Welfare Models of Disorder, Disability and Dependency versus User or Consumer Choice

60   At times of psychological crisis and in instances of continuing need, it is essential and proper for there to be dependency on support and treatment services. But, how does this connect with choice, when users may be unable to make informed choices, and when the choice of services available is limited?

Empowered Professionals and Managers versus Disempowered Users and Carers

61   One development of the past 20 years has been a reduction in the social distance between the professional and managerial staff of services and the patients, clients or users of those services. Experience has shown that staff at all levels must feel empowered before they can work towards the empowerment of users and carers. Equally, the latter must have a reasonable allocation of resources and training if they are to experience genuine empowerment.

Users versus Carers

62   Tensions between users of services and their carers are referred to rarely, but they are a reality. Users and carers are not a single homogeneous group, and there are times when their respective needs and interests diverge and may conflict.

Representation versus Accountability

63   Within this tension lie a number of key questions in which principles appear to be in competition. How representative are individual users or carers, and how are their representatives selected? There are risks that come from allocating responsibility for all users' views to a single representative (either individual, association or group). Similarly, there is an equal risk of stereotyping users' views. No single agency can represent all users or all of its members' personal views. In this circumstance, how best to gain user and carer opinions poses a predicament. Naturally, there can be a tendency to regard users' views positively when they agree with those of service managers. Similarly, unpopular views may be invalidated by virtue of their user status. The obverse also applies; if users are directly involved in commissioning and delivering services, does their user status free them from blame, when services fail? What protection is there for users as planners and managers and how are they to share in the success and responsibility for services?

Resources for Users and Carers and Their Groups

64   Goss and Miller (1995) opine that, *"The partnership between carers/users and workers must be equal in power but unequal in effort"*. Providing resources to support users and carers in contributing to services is not simply a financial issue. The foremost resource is time. Also, users and carers cannot be expected to match the skills and confidence of their professional counterparts, despite the expertise of users and carers in their own roles, without training and support. Office space and secretarial support are basic necessities.

65   As an illustration, the range of services purchased by one user-group is illuminating. Its members contracted for interpreters, signing materials, telephone calls, secretarial help, respite care, hotel accommodation, training (in management, disability awareness, counselling) and external consultants.

66   While the emphasis should be on the practical perspective of users and carers, their development as potential commissioners and providers involves some necessary risk-taking. The use of user and carer advocates at planning and review meetings may be helpful.

67   Where funding for support services is needed, to improve the involvement of users and carers, this should come from health authorities, trusts and local authority social services departments, and should be continuous. One study of carers (Warner, 1995) recommended Carer Initiative Grants to help to stimulate information dissemination, helplines and local carer groups.

68   Support for user and carer groups may also be made available by their linking with existing voluntary sector organisations such as MIND.

SUMMARY

69   The two sections above illustrate a number of the issues that arise when developing user and carer involvement. Each of these issues has been identified in the practical processes of encouraging and enabling better user and carer participation.

70   In some instances, the tensions, and particularly the matter of resources, describe matters that have to be solved before user and carer involvement can progress. Others of these tensions describe principles and practical matters wherein the tension, if well handled, can be productive of progress, valued influence and energy.

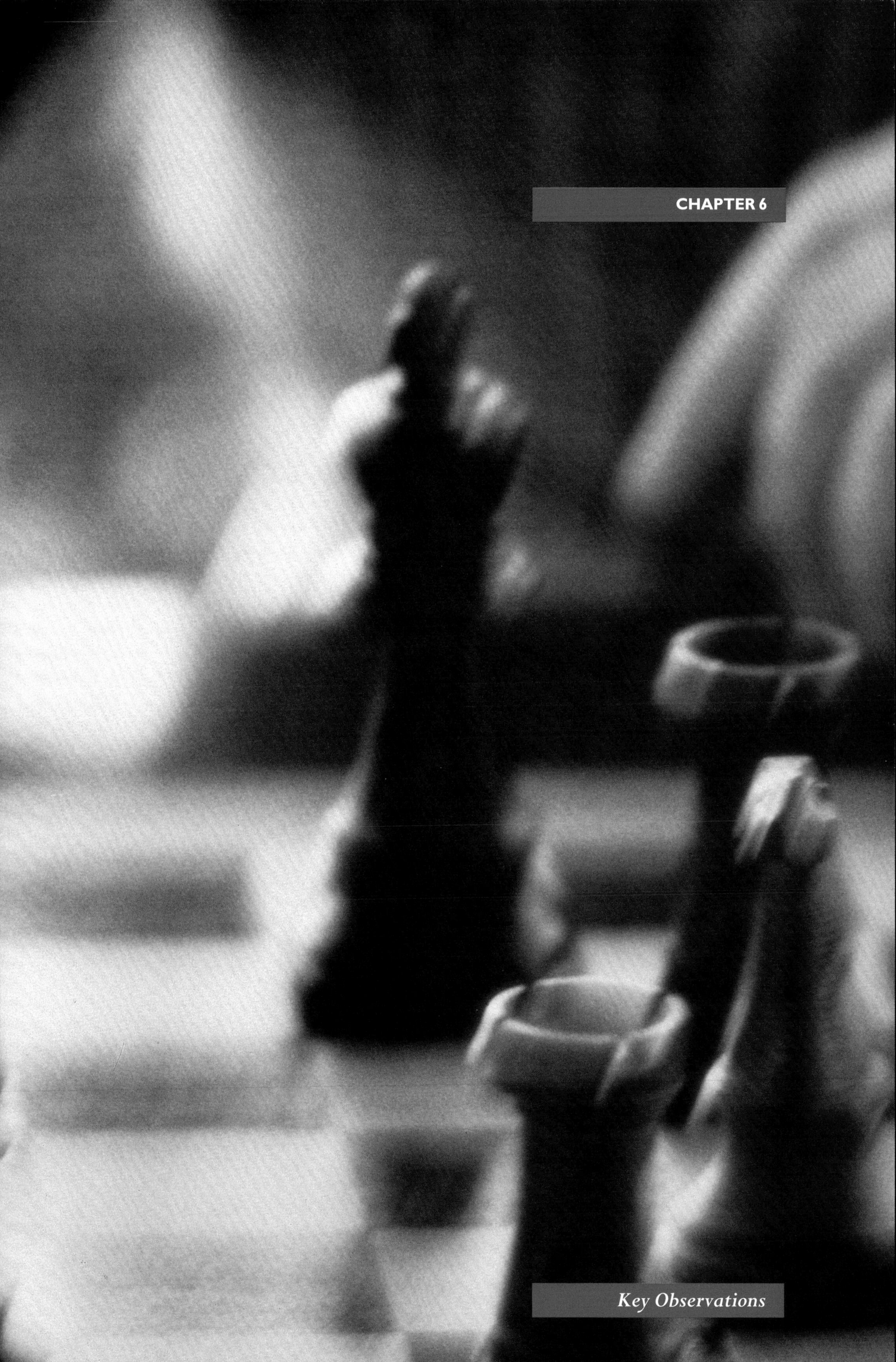

CHAPTER 6

Key Observations

INTRODUCTION

71   This chapter summarises key issues that come to the fore from the various sources of information reviewed by the HAS and in the site visits and reviews conducted on behalf of the HAS.

THE OPINIONS OF CARERS

72   Dissatisfaction among carers about support from service agencies is well-founded. One recent study (Warner, 1995) showed that:

- only one in five local authority social services departments has a carers' helpline;

- access to residential or nursing care has become more difficult over recent years;

- fewer than one in nine local authority social services departments provides a weekly break for carers;

- 80% of carers feel that the community care changes have made no difference;

- one in eight carers cancelled social services department help, with more than 40% opting for help from private services.

73   Since local authority social services departments have a major responsibility for providing services for community-based users, it is encouraging that this same study showed that 80% of carers felt that their social services department's services were reliable. However, about 50% of carers felt that access to social services departments for information or advice was difficult.

74   Nonetheless, carers appear to have clearly articulated a narrow set of minimum needs. These include:

- four hours break per week;

- one weekend break per month;

- a 24-hour helpline; and

- membership of a local carers' group.

75   A significant number of carers would like a core package of practical and monetary provision, which they can use flexibly, as needed (Warner, 1994). The subjects of this study were people who were caring for others with a wide range of disabilities including:

- elderly people;

- people with learning disabilities;

- people with physical handicaps; and

- people with a mental illness.

Nevertheless, the set of basic needs outlined above was common across all carer groups.

76   Payment for services is levied inconsistently. More worrying perhaps, some social services departments may be assessing and charging carers unlawfully. Under *Section 17* of the *Health and Social Services and Social Security Adjudications Act 1983*, local authorities have a discretionary power to charge adult recipients of non-residential services such as domiciliary, day and respite care. The *National Assistance Act 1948* gives local authorities the power to charge for residential care. But the *Mental Health Act 1983* confers no powers to charge for assessments, advice or after-care.
'...carers' income and savings cannot be taken into account in assessing charges payable for services provided to the person receiving care; and indeed...local authorities have no powers to levy charges unless they (carers) have received services themselves.' (Warner, 1995).

77   Despite this, Warner showed that 29% of carers' own incomes had been assessed for receipt of services, and the same proportion of carers' and users' joint incomes had been similarly assessed. The lot of carers is not helped by a lack of written assessments, these being provided by only 46% of social services departments in the study cited. It is difficult for carers to challenge decisions about charges without a written assessment.

78   The legal rights of carers for services are insufficiently supported by resources. This would seem to be an appropriate area for advocacy. The advent of the *Carers (Recognition and Services) Act 1995*, which took effect from 1 April 1996, should prompt statutory agencies to address carers' needs more vigorously, but the financial pressures that are faced by most of these agencies may well constrain the range and quality of help available.

79   Although carers themselves are often elderly, there seems to be no forward planning which addresses the long-term future of sick or elderly carers.

THE OPINIONS OF USERS

80   While there is some emerging evidence of users developing a political voice via well-structured and formal organisation of members, eg Gwynedd and Nottingham, user-power nationally is still in its infancy. Lack of funding to support users in these roles is a key problem.

81   Advocacy may be a means of ensuring that users' views are brought into planning processes generally, as well as ensuring their contribution to care planning when users themselves are ill or in crisis.

82 There is a crucial disjunction between the ethos of community care (as community-based provision) and the proper management of risk, with the accompanying need for clinical treatment and refuge (hospital care, or its equivalent). The pressure to manage and treat people on an outpatient basis has been accompanied by a corresponding pressure from diminishing inpatient facilities. Practically, however, the need for hospital places is likely to continue, as an essential component in a widening range of emergency and acute services.

AN OVERVIEW OF THE EXPERIENCES OF THE HAS

The Roles of Users and Carers

83 Recurrently, the teams employed by the HAS to review local services have recommended that users and carers be more involved at all levels of service commissioning, purchasing, planning and delivery. The teams' reports envisage their working at a number of levels and with a number of agencies covering, for instance, work with senior planners in social services departments and commissioners in health authorities, through to their greater involvement in planning their own individual care provision and its evaluation.

84 User and carer groups are already well-developed in some areas (eg Nottingham and Gwynedd) and are organised as companies that produce annual reports. In these circumstances the perceived imbalances of power between statutory agencies and users and carers is beginning to dissipate. However, young people and ethnic minorities are under-represented in the reports of both carer and user activities. This may reflect the under-provision of services for them as well as lesser levels of user and carer involvement.

The Position of Young People, Young Adults, Elderly People and People from Ethnic Minorities

85 Although this review focuses on the needs of adult users of mental health services, there are sub-groups of people whose needs are under-represented at all levels. The BRIJ review on mental health services for young people commissioned by the HAS (BRIJ, 1996) for instance, paints a picture of severe social and psychological vulnerability among young people, whose needs seem to be disappearing into a service void. One of that review team's findings was that vulnerable 16- and 17-year olds were characterised as:

- uncommunicative and withdrawn;

- prone to self-harm, including deliberate self-harm;

- experiencing abusive relationships (including prostitution based on using drugs as a currency);

- misusing alcohol and/or drugs; and

- in some instances, suffering from eating disorders or more severe mental disorder, and having difficulty obtaining professional diagnoses.

86   This evidence suggests that young people with serious mental disorder in the 16 to 18 years age-range are very vulnerable. They are too young for proper welfare entitlements, as well as for adult psychiatric services. There is a great risk of vulnerable people of this age drifting into a despairing decline of continuous homelessness, crime and worsening mental health. Their vulnerability can continue for many years. Extending the age definition of young person up to 25 years and developing appropriate services for their specialist needs could reduce the potential for them to slip through the mental health services net as easily as they do now.

87   Other groups, whose needs are not specifically addressed in this brief review, are elderly people and those of ethnic minorities. A brief case report (Jansari, 1993) illustrates how age and ethnic factors can combine to pose particular service problems. That report highlights the care given by an Indian man and his sister to their elderly parents. As Hindus, the children were under a moral duty to care for their parents, who were both severely disabled, vegan and spoke no English. Mainstream day centres are mainly English-speaking, so the parents were not able to continue attending them. Neither the parents nor their son and daughter had had a holiday for many years. The stress on both children was intense, and no respite or alternative care had been assessed as necessary. On this evidence alone, appropriate care plans should take into account:

- language;

- family custom;

- religion and prayer;

- timing of waking and eating; and

- the parents' worries about any absences of the son or daughter, whether for respite or for the latters' need to attend to their own families.

The Consequent Responsibilities of Users and Carers

88   Representation and involvement bring responsibilities. If an accepted principle of social justice is that users and carers have a right to have their needs assessed and met and to participate in this process, they also take on consequent responsibilities. Once involved in commissioning, planning and delivering services, users and carers may accrue accountabilities to tax payers and to the voting public that are similar to those of service employees.

Progress in Implementing Greater Involvement of Users and Carers

89   Progress has been made. More than ever, assessment processes are needs-based. But there is a continuing tendency for the opinions of the perceived experts to take precedence over the wishes of service users. Similarly, there are few services that have systematic means for evaluating consumer satisfaction. Currently, many assessment instruments address symptomatology and behaviour but, often, they fail to solicit users' and carers' perceptions.

90   Inter-agency co-ordination presents a bewildering array of obstacles. In England, for instance, there are challenges to providers of different agencies in co-ordinating action on the care programme approach, care management and the supervision register. Users and carers are often caught in the middle of what they perceive to be an organisational muddle. To this are added the differing perspectives of social services departments and health authorities, with the former planning around individual user needs, and the latter commissioning for the needs of cohorts of patients.

91   In some districts, the care programme approach is having a major bottom-up impact on mainstream mental health services. Nevertheless, it suffers from being a top- down, central government initiative that was perceived as an imposition by professionals and users and carers for many years after its introduction. Although the care programme approach is intended to enable users and carers to have a direct voice in care planning and delivery, and to track any shortfall in provision, its implementation has been slow and uneven, possibly as a consequence. Nonetheless, the value of the care programme approach has begun to make an impact on service design and functioning.

92   HAS reports cite the facilities required by user and carer groups. These include secretarial and computing assistance, databases and book-keeping. Time, funding and training to develop clinical awareness and planning and managerial skills are also required. These needs must be built into services when they are designed and planned. However, without a local strategic mental health policy, there is no basis on which to encourage user and carer involvement, still less to ensure that users and carers can negotiate on an equal footing. One recent study revealed that effectively two-thirds of health authorities had no such strategic plan (Huxley and Hoser, 1996).

93   However, when funding is sufficient to support and remunerate carers and users, there is a danger of creating professional users and carers. As such, their views may become unrepresentative and distanced from the wider body of service users or have disproportionate influence.

94   In retrospect, while the positions of the HAS review teams seem to have been very similar, there are some differences in their perspectives. One team favoured strong advocacy, but saw the main responsibility for services as resting with providers, and placed little value on the inclusion of users in the commissioning process. Some user and carer groups favoured the exclusion of professionals, except for co-opted consultants, while yet other groups preferred the involvement of professionals and viewed them as allies. The latter groups tended to see their worth in terms of immediate benefits to members (supportive and therapeutic), rather than as lobbying bodies. Plainly, there is a spectrum of opinion as to mechanisms for seeking the involvement of users in service evaluation, commissioning and delivery and a spectrum of roles that they might play. This mixed picture suggests that coalitions between user, carer and professional groups are new, cautious but developing gradually.

*An Analysis
of the
Current Circumstances*

CHAPTER 7

The Roles of
Users and Carers

INTRODUCTION

95   In this chapter, the report seeks to open up the matters considered in chapter 5, which examines the tensions implicit and/or explicit in rebalancing the positions held by service consumers and the staff of those services, and chapter 6 which adds information from the literature and the experience of the HAS.

96   Based on these lessons and research, the core issue considered in this chapter concerns how users might effectively develop their voices through lobbying and/or as advocates and thereby have an impact on the professional commissioners and providers of services. Later, in chapters 10, 11 and 12, this report considers these matters again but at a greater level of detail in relationship to three key areas of service functioning.

LOBBYING AND PRESSURE GROUPS – DEVELOPING A VOICE

Purposes

97   Although there are many potential tensions resulting from the involvement of users and carers in commissioning and delivering services, the core purpose of their involvement is to improve the sensitivity, direction and appropriateness of:

- service design and composition;
- service development;
- commissioning and purchasing;
- the range of services commissioned and delivered;
- quality standards;
- the delivery of patient care.

98   Related reasons for promoting the involvement of users and carers in service commissioning and delivery include:

- the intrinsic therapeutic value of these endeavours;
- the protection of civil rights, liberation and empowerment; and
- ensuring that the voices of users and carers as experts in defining their own wishes and needs are heard.

Initiating the Involvement of Users and Carers

99   The process of initiating the involvement of users and carers with the responsible bodies can involve direct or indirect methods (LeTouze, 1993). Direct methods include:

- appointment of users' or carers' support workers;
- construction of networks of users and carers;
- construction of registers of users and carers;
- involving users and carers in writing community care plans, social care plans and children's plans;

- training users and carers to represent their own interests; and

- involving users and carers in training professionals.

100   Indirect methods of involving users and carers include:

- improving publicity and information provided for the public about services;

- provision of helplines;

- developing resource centres for users and carers;

- aiding users and carers to form groups.

101   Many of these processes require replacement carers, as well as transport, to be made available in order to enable individuals to find the time required to present their opinions and undertake more specific activities.

102   At the local level, collective activity can begin with establishing a special interest or steering group relating to user and carer representation. Its activities might include:

- the formal establishment of a user and carer group;

- conducting a survey of user views;

- setting up a forum to discuss the results of surveys and to decide on the next steps;

- dissemination of the results of user surveys by means of a briefing document or report.

At the formative stage some groups may choose to exclude professionals or other experts.

103   Groups of this kind need a base, office space, administrative support and funding. The latter might come from the NHS, or a local authority.

104   As such a group develops a sense of identity and purpose, it is able to begin to relate effectively to professional stakeholders – key managers and professional staff who are opinion leaders in service commissioning and provision. At this stage, a survey document, statement of aims or mission statement may be a useful focus for this engagement.

Targets and Intentions

105   Further development of user and/or carer groups is enhanced by clarifying their targets and intentions. A group's interests may be aimed at specific targets, such as individual service managers within provider units, or at more general audiences, for instance, through awareness training days, conferences and stakeholder meetings with health and social services commissioners.

106   On the other hand, engagement with broader audiences can be used to address a number of issues, such as:

Education

In this instance, education is intended to increase the awareness of professionals about user and carer opinions, and the potential for their involvement through contributing to their training and continuing professional development. In this way, greater contacts with users and carers in settings outside direct service-related encounters may also powerfully influence the attitudes of professionals.

Communication

Creating a forum for continuing dialogue between users and carers and professionals relating to current issues and concerns, set against the structural, organisational and resource constraints faced by providers, may also have powerful beneficial effects on service delivery.

Public Relations

Raised public awareness by positive promotion of mental health issues may also ensue from user and carer involvement. Indeed, tackling matters such as stigma may be a primary target.

Political Influence

Political influence may be achieved by users and carers by a combination of individual lobbying (of local councillors or Members of Parliament), gaining media support and collective campaigning. Directing activity at increasing political influence may lead to the development of a locally or nationally recognised group, and some may eventually also offer their own services. Examples include NAFSIYAT, a trans-cultural psychotherapy service based in London; the Afro-Caribbean Mental Health Association; MIND; the UK Advocacy Network; Survivors Speak Out; the Manic-depression Fellowship; and other similar organisations.

Continued Support and Longevity

107   In order for the membership and interests of user and/or carer groups to develop and thrive after the initial stages, continued support will be necessary, with the possible alliance of the group with voluntary sector bodies such as MIND, the Carers National Association, or the National Schizophrenia Fellowship.

108   Experience indicates that certain key issues may determine the course, longevity and influence of local groups of this nature. The main ones are listed and described here:

Leadership and Motivation

Rivalry and conflict can be offset by shared leadership, either by having a convener to assemble and chair meetings, and a driver to ensure agreed actions are undertaken, or by members taking turns at leadership. Generally, groups require at least one or two people with unusual energy and durability to sustain motivation. Whether or not a professional should take on this role, if so requested, is open to debate; outside influence may be perceived as paternalistic and patronising as easily as it may be perceived as impartial and facilitating.

- **Representation and Access**
  The principle of users and carers having access to all levels of relevant organisations is sound. However, it is unlikely to occur overnight, and may not always be useful unless some preliminary steps towards representation have been taken. These steps might include identification of the users most suited to represent their group, or preparation of users for high level negotiations. Nevertheless, the demand for representation and access is likely to continue, and may contrast with the principle adopted by some groups of excluding professionals from their group meetings.

- **Conflicting Interests**
  Users' and carers' interests coincide on many issues. Nonetheless, it is important to recognise that this is not the case on all matters, on all occasions, or in all instances. Therefore, user and carer representation should not be interchangeable. In many circumstances, separate representation, separate representative groups and their separate involvement in service commissioning and delivery is more appropriate. Added role confusion and potential for conflict can occur where a user is also a carer.

- **Vulnerability**
  Most user and carer groups are set up to meet a variety of needs or objectives. Quite often they combine a campaigning, action-orientated function with supportive and therapeutic functions. The division or combination of tasks is important and combinations can challenge the stance and direction of local as well as national associations. However, the more a group anticipates the differing demands of the range of tasks it takes on, the less likely is conflict to arise within its membership.

- **Professional Equality**
  A challenge that is becoming more evident as the user and carer movements mature, concerns the question of when users and carers are considered to have become salaried professionals. The development of paid user or carer representatives has been slow in the UK compared to the USA. Nonetheless, this change in the status of users and carers is likely to become a more significant matter in the next century.

ADVOCACY

109   *The Carers (Recognition and Services) Act 1995* illustrates how effective advocacy at a political level can be, insofar as the Carers National Association has been substantially responsible for the lobbying and publicity which has resulted in this Act.

110   At more local levels, paid independent advocacy can ensure that users have impartial witnesses and supporters. Some of the problems that are currently experienced by users with the present arrangements for advocacy include:

- confusion about the advocate role when the chosen person is also a service professional, such as a social worker or a community psychiatric nurse;

- confusion over the varieties of service, and how to choose them, eg the Citizens Advice Bureau (CAB), solicitor, law centre etc;

- fears about the risks of daring to voice a dissenting opinion about services (many users fear that by so doing they might risk jeopardising their own care or support);

- complaints procedures, including employing procedures established under the auspices of the *Patient's Charter*, are not considered by many users to be the answer they were initially thought to be. Examples of reported problems with current procedures include their tone, their relevance when the user is vulnerable to formal admission, and the finding by many users that agency responses are slow and palliative.

111   Some agencies (for example Ashworth Hospital and the Family Welfare Association) have employed professional, bespoke advocacy services. These might be considered as models for other mental health organisations. Services of this kind do more than act as advocates for individual users. They support the development of patients' groups and influence hospital practice generally by commenting on operational policies and practices. The range of other advocacy activities in one such service covers:

- increasing the availability of clinical assessments, including access to neurological assessment, psychology, dentistry and other services;

- involving the participation of patients and their relatives in care planning;

- urging better organised rehabilitation programmes and home visits;

- establishing better communication between patients and their psychiatrists, as well as among staff teams;

- providing more support, training and supervision for staff; and

- promoting greater awareness of the special problems of patients from ethnic minority groups.

112   There is an extremely high degree of skill and suppleness required to develop user and carer groups, as well as in enabling their incorporation in service provision at individual, programme and strategic levels. Being a willing advocate is not enough.

113   Some consider that there is a place for a specialist role, equivalent to that of an NHS consultant. If suggestions of this nature were to gain support, appointees could not be radical ombudsmen. Rather, they would occupy responsible, authoritative posts designed to carry credibility with users, carers and the staff of services.

114   This suggestion illustrates the importance of identifying those elements of activity which promote user/carer involvement, and those which hamper it. These issues arise in groups which address commissioning and providing, as well as in user and carer groups. All advocates should ensure that the user/carer agenda is sensible and realistic and unlikely to lead them into stereotypical roles or actions. Neither should it be assumed that users or carers are their own best advocates just because they are users or carers.

COMMISSIONING

Commissioning, Purchasing and Contracting

115   There is a tendency to use the words *commissioning, purchasing* and *contracting* interchangeably. And the guideline document, *Purchasing for Health* (NHS Management Executive, 1993), uses the term *purchasing* generally.

116   In this review, *commissioning* is the umbrella term, emphasising strategy. We take it to mean a strategically driven process by which purchasers (health authorities, GP fundholders, social services departments, etc) achieve the provision of services for their local population that are:

- tuned to its needs;

- sensitive to the opinions and advice of actual and potential service users and their informal carers;

- based upon an appreciation of the clinical realities;

- of defined and monitored key qualities; and

- evidence-based.

117   *Purchasing* refers to the various technical procedures carried out by purchasers to secure and monitor the services that they are commissioning from providers.

118   *Contracting*, a component of *purchasing*, is the process by which services are purchased and the negotiated natures and levels of services to be provided are confirmed by formal agreements. In effect, *commissioning* encompasses *purchasing* and *contracting* but also implies a greater range of tasks because it concerns strategy and involves attempts to monitor, define and manage the market, thus creating a circular process.

Commissioning and Purchasing in the NHS

119   The accumulated experience of the HAS since 1992 allows further observations to be made concerning the relationship between *commissioning, purchasing* and *contracting*. Contracting appears to be most effective in securing appropriate user and population-sensitive

services when it is used as a mechanism to consolidate agreements between purchasers and providers. It is less effective when used as a means of passing on performance indicators, forcing changes in service delivery patterns or managing performance. Thus, contracting appears to be most effective when it is used within a wider commissioning process in support of negotiated strategy and clear purchasing intentions. These observations support the importance of strategy and planning to health authorities and other commissioners in achieving their obligations. Otherwise, there is the possibility of contracting processes and currencies assuming undue importance in the relationships between commissioners and purchasers and their providers. This can risk detailed items in contracts and the contracting mechanisms themselves driving the healthcare agenda rather than the overall intentions of commissioners and purchasers guiding the way forward, with services being delivered on the basis of mature purchaser-provider relationships.

120   This is not to negate the importance of a sound performance management framework. Rather, the experience of the HAS is that performance indicators are best implemented through negotiation and by ensuring that they have face validity as well as coherence with, and relevance to, strategic intentions.

121   Since the implementation of the *NHS and Community Care Act 1990,* there has been a dynamic force in the system responsible for moving the purchasing of healthcare as close to patients as possible. This has led to health authorities and GP fundholders experiencing shifts in the scope of their role as both commissioners and purchasers. EL(94)79, *Towards a Primary Care-led NHS,* sets out an agenda that sees the health authorities (since 1 April 1996 these are the amalgamations of the old health authorities and family health services authorities (FHSAs)) taking the responsibility for commissioning at a strategic level, informed by the public and their providers (including GPs), while increasing the direct responsibility of general practitioner fundholders as purchasers. Following this system, health authorities act primarily as the commissioners, while retaining some direct purchasing responsibilities (increasingly for more specialised services), and GP fundholders act as major direct purchasers, while retaining the role of informing commissioning decisions. In order to accommodate this process of change, this thematic review uses the terms *commissioning* and *purchasing* to describe functions rather than to prescribe them to any one agency.

122   Health authorities are being urged to move away from the extra-contractual referral (ECR) of individuals or small numbers of cases. The alternative approaches involve a variety of techniques, including consortium and lead purchasing or the delegation of established extra-contractual referral budgets to providers, with the intention of redistributing the financial risks.

The Key Principles of Effective Commissioning in the NHS

123   The ultimate aim of commissioning is to improve the health of the population while increasing user satisfaction with health services. To achieve this, health authorities should:

- formulate a strategy which outlines the priorities, the actions to be taken and desired outcomes in order to produce better healthcare for people with a mental illness;

- work with other purchasers (social services departments and GP fundholders) to implement the strategy through purchasing mechanisms supported by mature contracts;

- work with NHS, not-for-profit and private sector providers to improve the quality and efficiency of current services and to develop new and more effective services in place of those which are shown to be ineffective;

- work with the representatives of people generally, service users and their carers in order to ensure that the strategy for mental health services and the nature and quality of service delivery are sensitive to their advice and opinions; and

- collaborate with the local community and other statutory, voluntary and independent sector organisations to ensure that service delivery is co-ordinated and seamless.

Commissioning and Purchasing by Local Authorities

124   It is important to recognise the differences of approach that are being taken, generally, by local and health authorities. The former, with conspicuous responsibilities for care management, are required to purchase packages of care for individuals, while health authorities buy sectors of care for populations. One result of this difference is that the assessment of individuals is a significant part of the purchasing role in the case of local authorities, while it lies almost entirely within the provider province in the NHS.

125   From a social services perspective, the commissioning process may be considered to be direct or indirect. Indirect commissioning describes the actions of purchasers in which decisions are translated into service provision by purchasing them from providers and by contracting out. Direct commissioning means making payments to clients directly. The payments made may be dependent on users' available capital and determined by means-testing. In time, clients then engage their own service providers. This may be combined with the provision of some services through indirect commissioning to constitute a core package of money and services. Most carers report higher satisfaction with direct commissioning, in terms of improved quality and flexibility of support. Direct commissioning is also said to be appreciably cheaper than indirect commissioning.

126   Despite the differences in approach between local and health authorities, which must be surmounted through jointly agreed strategies and priorities and through the co-ordination of care for individuals, local authorities and health purchasers are being encouraged towards joint commissioning.

Commissioning and Purchasing and the Roles of Users and Carers

127 Plainly, the tasks of commissioning and purchasing services are complex ones involving a variety of processes, and users and carers may have much to contribute in respect of each component. Moreover, as already identified, the requirements of commissioning and purchasing, and therefore the concepts within them, differ between the NHS and local authorities.

128 Thus the purchaser-provider system, and the many different ways in which its detail has been implemented across the country, presents a bewildering array of functions, systems and processes for service users, their carers and staff alike. However, this mechanism does open up the possibilities of much more systematic involvement of users and carers in influencing the design of services, as well as what is bought for populations and for individuals.

129 Moves towards joint commissioning by health authorities and local authority social services departments are increasingly popular. This is an opportune time for users and carers to be included in what is still an embryonic process.

130 Whatever model is adopted locally it is important that commissioners and purchasers tune their approaches across sectors of care as well as with the opinions of their other sources of information and with the views of users, carers, local leaders of opinion, professionals and managers so that the strategy, service delivery and quality targets for local services are informed by the clinical realities, by clinical evidence and by user and carer opinion.

131 Users and carers might improve their standing and their influence on commissioners by:

- providing briefings and opinions, perhaps through workshops, for commissioning managers;
- direct negotiations with social services departments and NHS managers about the opinions of users and carers on the quality of current services and on desirable directions for the future.

INFLUENCING SERVICE MANAGEMENT AND DELIVERY – GETTING APPROPRIATE SERVICES FOR ONESELF

132 Before user/carer involvement permeates all mental health services as a result of concerted activity, the particularly vocal or higher profile users and carers are more likely to have their opinions heard. For individual users, this remains the central day-to-day objective.

133   Now that the care programme approach requires explicit care plans to be drawn up and shared with users, there is a stronger probability of user feedback being sought and incorporated into decision making and into service information systems. This will have the secondary benefit of helping services to track and influence shortfall.

134   As well as this important form of passive user-involvement, there is the more active participation of users and carers in care planning. This is already encouraged within voluntary sector organisations, and has been brought into the NHS and social services departments by the care programme approach, care planning and, more recently, by the *Carers (Recognition and Services) Act 1995*.

135   However, experience shows that when users and/or their carers are dissatisfied with local provision, self-help may be the answer. In some localities, individual self-help has grown via groups promoting alternative care systems (such as the Manchester Alliance for Community Care).

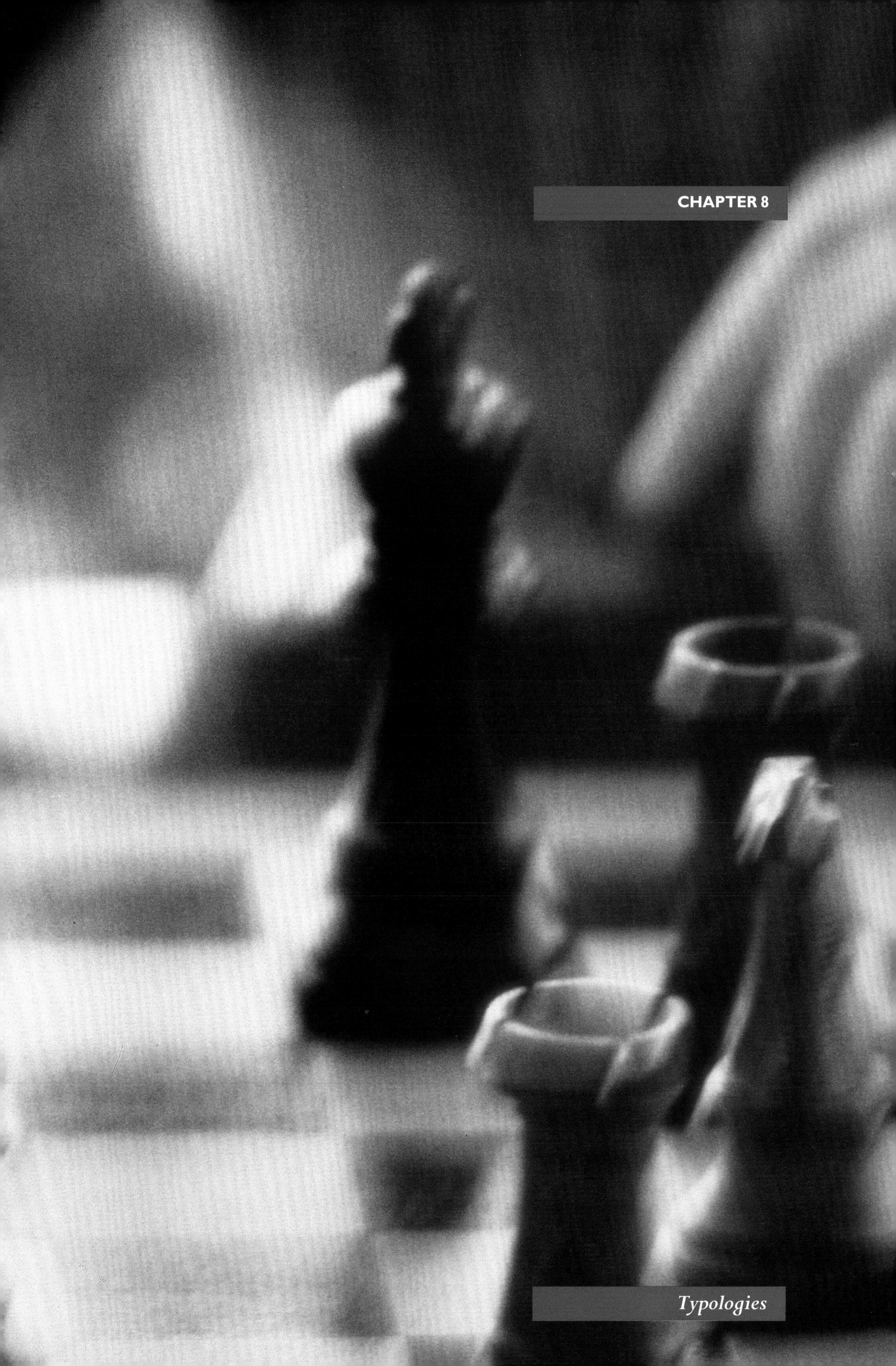

CHAPTER 8

Typologies

INTRODUCTION

136   At its core, this review has highlighted the changing interfaces between the users of mental health services, their carers and the staff of those services. The report has considered a review of some of the literature, the experiences of the HAS and the tensions in developing the roles of users and carers and how they might develop more powerful and potent voices in a variety of roles.

137   Before going on to explore some aspects of these roles in more depth, we summarise matters covered so far by examining two particular ways of construing these interfaces.

138   Thereafter, the authors identify and briefly illustrate the meaning of some eight criteria that might be applied when considering the roles and impacts of users and carers on mental health services. In effect, these criteria frame a third typology for understanding the changed interfaces between users, carers and the employees of services.

INTERFACES – TWO TYPOLOGIES

139   There are several ways of understanding the interface of groups of users and carers with the staff of mental health services, and how this interface might flourish. One way is to examine the nature of the relationship between users and carers and professional services (Goss and Miller, 1995). This can be illustrated by a continuum of user and carer involvement in service planning, from least to greatest. Table 2 indicates such a spectrum of involvement which has been modified for this publication.

Table 2

Levels of User and Carer Involvement in Service Planning		
Type of involvement	**Nature of involvement**	**Level of involvement** Least ▲
NO INVOLVEMENT	So-called take-it-or-leave-it planning (from the perspective of users and carers).	
INFORMATION AND PUBLIC RELATIONS	Consumer education and marketing of services. Staff develop solutions. Communication is essentially one way.	
CONSULTATION	Market research and limited two-way communication with users and carers. Staff develop options and consult users and carers, but they also make their own recommendations to professionals and service commissioners.	
CONSULTATION AND AGENDA SETTING	Listening and responsive systems in which there is open and wide ranging consultation and users and carers are involved in the analysis of problems and in proposing and assessing options for their solution.	
JOINT PLANNING	Collaborative definition of problems including pooled information, combined decisions and conjoint working.	
USER AND CARER CONTROL	No model currently in operation.	▼ Greatest

140 Another typology is that of Huxley (1996), which is derived from an exhaustive review of the literature on user representation, and which draws substantially from North American models. The typology focuses on imbalances of power in service systems, as these affect the capacities of users to influence service planning and provision. The typology provides a three-tier axis, with least power residing at the lowest (individual) level, and most power residing at the highest (system) level.

141 Each level of user or carer service interface can be characterised as having one of three aims:

- **Information**
  The information provided to users and carers is aimed at improving communication about mental health and related services.

- **Participation**
  The aim of participation is that users and carers have increasing involvement in decision-making.

- **Opposition**
  This is the position taken by abolitionists who are dedicated to the elimination of the psychiatric service system and to influencing the social accommodation of mentally ill people. This is the position of those who would like a reduction in the amount of influence exerted by current psychiatric systems and professionals, and who want to see the accommodation rather than separation of mentally ill people in the social mainstream.

142 Some of the types of activities undertaken as part of user involvement in service planning, within this second typology, are illustrated in Table 3. In essence, Huxley's typology endeavours to locate and describe user and carer involvement by reference to two axes – one describes the level of involvement and the second is that of its aim. Thus the type of each scheme of user or carer involvement may be described by reference to these two axes.

Table 3

Types of User and Carer Involvement in Service Planning			
LEVEL	**AIM OR TYPE**		
	Information	**Participation**	**Opposition**
System	Charters and standards	Commissioning, planning and purchasing	Reformation of current service patterns
Programme	Booklets, leaflets, surveys	Providing care and treatment	Competition
Individual	Feedback	Care planning	Self-help

143 Users and carers may possess information and have an understanding about organisations and service planning, but this is not the same as using their own capacities to participate in their own care or in service planning. Some of these differences, as they appear at system, programme and individual levels, have been examined earlier. However, oppositional approaches to service planning have not been examined and these may have some relevance here, in respect of describing the activities conducted by some users and carers.

144 At the systems level, exponents of oppositional approaches view current mainstream mental health systems as inherently oppressive and resistant to change. Stigma arising from user status is laid at the door of psychiatry rather than society. Similarly, social rather than medical policies are held to be deficient for failing to address basic needs of income, housing and other (non-psychiatric) resources.

145 At the programme level, oppositionists view user involvement as an adversarial endeavour with, for example, the consultant psychiatrist viewed as the powerful defender of the status quo, and the user as the powerless recipient of service.

146 At the individual level, oppositionists view self-help as contrary to the policies and practices of standard services. It is here that oppositional thinking seems to become muddled since an aim of most standard services is independent functioning and self-care by users. Similarly, self-help is more of a concept than a model of care. Nevertheless, oppositionists have had an important voice in the user movement, and varieties of self-help have particularly encouraged collective empowerment and combated stigma among users.

147 Certain forms of campaigning can be regarded as the constructive front of oppositional approaches. Although many are local in origin and impact, some campaigning groups, such as Survivors Speak Out, have already developed into durable political entities of national significance.

CRITERIA

Rhetoric and Reality

148 This section surveys briefly some of the criteria that have been used in exploring the nature and impacts of user and carer involvement.

149 There is a substantial and still burgeoning literature on user and carer involvement, but very little consideration of its impact. Words such as empowerment, representation and participation are used frequently and imply social movements of great weight. Looking beyond the rhetoric, however, what has been their effect on altering the organisation and delivery of services, and has this, in turn, had any effect on mental health? Currently, the evidence in this country is not encouraging, for many different reasons, some of which are outlined below.

Participation

150 Participation may be therapeutic in itself, but not every user and carer wants to be involved, nor does every user and carer experience beneficial effects through their involvement.

Competition

151 Competition connotes rivalry – user-provided services could compete with statutory services and this could create challenges at the systems level. The risk is that service planning could then become oppositional, with users, carers and providers occupying separate businesses, rather than it being a participative exercise based on negotiation.

Continuity

152 Continuity is notoriously poor in many services, with high worker turnover and a continuing emphasis on client turnover and short-term care and treatment.

Practical versus Emotional Help

153 There is a mismatch between material aid and personal care; the former is functional while the latter is subjective and inter-personal. Service change needs simultaneously to address personal change in individual users, who may not welcome or be able to accept personal or situational change, merely because a new service requires this.

Organisational Change versus Outcome Change

154 More needs to be known about the processes for involving users and carers. Organisational change is often too reliant on one or two strongly motivated characters. However, for outcome change the destination needs to be clearer; is improved overall mental health the goal, or is the goal change in the ways in which services are delivered?

System Pragmatism

155 Many decisions made by purchasers and providers are reactive to the information available to them. Purchasers should be educated by consumers, as much as by service providers, as one HAS/SSI(W) service review noted:

"Purchasing is the key to effective services. It should be driven by user need rather than by provider preference." NHS Health Advisory Service and Social Services Inspectorate, Wales, 1994; *A Review of Services for Mentally Ill People in the South Glamorgan Health District.* Page 3, para 8(2).

Political and Administrative Will

156 The principle of user and carer involvement in planning and delivery is generally agreed, but is not yet a reality. The effects of such involvement, in terms of change in existing systems and improved overall mental health and quality of life for users and carers, is not very evident. A central difficulty is that, although new legislation espouses the cause of users and carers, this legislation is not accompanied by funding for the infrastructure changes needed to ensure that users and carers lead, rather than receive, services. Similarly, fiscal retrenchment may have an indirect impact in that only the most able users and carers are likely to be able to pursue their aims without additional funded support.

Summary

157 If user and carer involvement does inform service and mental health changes, what are the published results of this from places where user involvement is better established? One academic commentator, at least, remains unable to find sufficient evidence to draw conclusions currently:

"In general, it is impossible to tell from the written material." (Huxley, 1996).

CHAPTER 9

A Summary of the Analysis

INTRODUCTION

158   If the previous chapter finished on an uncertain downbeat note, this does not represent any scepticism of the HAS about the value and importance of user and carer involvement. What is described in this report is the current position – one of diffuse, patchy, early development in which there are a wide variety of issues that are at play in respect of user and carer influence. The intention of this narrative is to provide readers with an account of the present position in a very mobile and changing scene. Also, the report endeavours to provide a summary of lessons and experience and to identify some of the conceptual issues and possible frameworks for future comparisons and analyses.

159   The experiences of the HAS, the literature and the criteria considered in the chapter on typology indicate that there are several broad headings under which the issues might be construed. They include:

- the intentions, aims, desires and motives of users and carers in seeking greater influence – these are revealed by typology of the levels of user and carer involvement and by Huxley's three-tier model;

- the impact of user and carer involvement;

- the attitudes, responses and positions of the responsible authorities and of individual members of staff;

- the support and training provided for users and for carers;

- other unpredicted or unintended, even perverse, potential and actual influences – some of these are revealed when examining the criteria in the second half of chapter 8.

160   Nonetheless, the HAS review has revealed the areas in which user and carer activity has already developed. The situation is very variable across the country. The remainder of this brief summary lists those general areas of user and carer involvement and the key factors that are thought to influence success.

AREAS OF SIGNIFICANT USER AND CARER INVOLVEMENT

161   Some significant areas of user and carer activity in respect of mental health services have emerged. These include:

- individual and collective lobbying, and alliances with larger and more powerful representative groups;

- advocacy of all kinds;

- the appointment of professional staff who are charged with promoting the involvement of users and carers. These staff may have generic tasks including gathering information on all carers, eg to develop a carer network or register, or they may have specific functions, eg setting up users' forums or collating evidence of the mental health needs of an ethnic minority group;

- commissioning and purchasing activity that is directly influenced by user and carer involvement;

- involving users and carers in performance management;

- involving users and carers in designing care programmes for individuals;

- situations in which users and carers are directly involved in and responsible for providing services.

SUCCESS FACTORS

162   Some key factors that appear from experience to influence the likely success of users and carers being involved in commissioning, planning and service delivery are:

- incorporating carers more in assessment processes;

- striking the right balance between professional and user and carer representation in discussion and planning meetings;

- providing funding for training, administrative and secretarial support, travel, expenses, office space, information systems for users and carers and their groups;

- open dialogue between professionals and users and carers, and between users and carers themselves;

- professional flexibility – many professionals will have to relearn their working habits and procedures acquired over years of traditional top-down service delivery methods, during which users' and carers' views may have been scarcely known. These new relationships with users and carers may be as refreshing as they are threatening and professionals require support, training and understanding in moving towards positions of flexibility. Already, the greater involvement of users and carers in contributing to training schemes for professionals appears a very positive step forward;

- professional advocacy, as distinct from other forms of user and carer participation. In one location (Ashworth Hospital), independent, professional advocates have addressed users' problems during care and at discharge. More significantly, they have also begun to collect data on discrepancies in patients welfare benefits entitlements, and are perceiving new ways in which the transfer of patients between court, prison and special hospital could be more equitably managed. This form of advocacy not only influences service planning and provision, but is also a potential influence on future legislation.

163   The evidence of the impact of user and carer activity in the field of adult mental health in the UK is scant. Two promising developments are:

- the greater credibility given to purchasers in Newcastle by the inclusion of users in planning services;

- the recent involvement in Nottingham of users and carers in a large-scale evaluative study of services.

*Developing some of
the Roles of
Users and Carers*

CHAPTER 10

*The Involvement of
Users and Carers
in the
Strategic Direction and
Development of Services*

INTRODUCTION

164 The gap is widening between rapidly developing professional capability and system capacity that is growing but less rapidly. There is also the potential for the choices inherent in this circumstance to produce greater variability of services and, possibly, adverse effects on their quality.

165 Some commentators allege that financial constraints on health authorities and local authority social services departments have meant that best care is being reduced to cheapest care, and unmet need is being redefined as unmet choice.

166 A recent study shows that one-third of social services departments have no record of the unmet needs of users. Assessment of the needs of the user in this same study (58% reported such assessments) clearly outweighed assessments of the needs of the carer (39%). In both cases, not enough services are regularly assessing needs (Warner, 1995).

167 All these circumstances emphasise the importance of a strategic overview of service delivery and of a commissioned approach to the selection of services that will be provided.

168 One of the tasks of commissioners is the challenge of selecting a direction and the consequent design of mental health services; then choosing priorities for the development of components of the intended services. The HAS model of commissioning emphasises the importance of balancing the views of users and carers with professional opinion and capability and with the evidence-base in making these choices. Thus, there are potent roles for users and carers in the commissioning process. Some of these are summarised in this chapter.

Figure 1

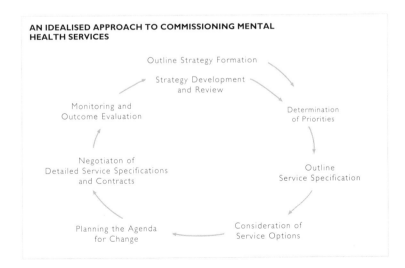

AN IDEALISED APPROACH TO COMMISSIONING MENTAL HEALTH SERVICES

Outline Strategy Formation

Strategy Development and Review

Monitoring and Outcome Evaluation

Determination of Priorities

Negotiaton of Detailed Service Specifications and Contracts

Outline Service Specification

Planning the Agenda for Change

Consideration of Service Options

Figure 2

169   The main processes in which users and carers are involved at this level are planning innovations to services, setting priorities (including making disinvestment and reinvestment decisions), helping to inform quality development programmes and defining service specifications.

170   One user group in the UK (in Nottingham) endorses advocacy as the most useful means of influencing strategic planning, with users sitting on project and development committees. Another user group (in Newcastle) has been working with purchasers whose credibility has been enhanced by user involvement. Experience indicates that this kind of proximity between planning and service use is the current extent of users acting as commissioners of mental health services.

PROGRAMME PLANNING

171   The approach espoused encompasses the involvement of users and carers at a variety of points in the commissioning process. Already, their strategic contribution has been emphasised. Nonetheless, it will be apparent that users and carers can have potent roles in the design of broad programmes of care and, through their engagement with providers, they may usefully bridge the gap between purchasers and providers in the purchasing and contracting processes and, less formally, in the dialogues between the responsible bodies. Practical influences on the direction and detail of programme design and evaluation can have real impact.

172 The benefits to users at this level may be therapeutic as well as instrumental, for example, for those people who experience social withdrawal, or anxiety disorders. However, some users may be unable to participate without support and in this circumstance appointment of an advocate would be appropriate.

173 There are a number of practical and interpersonal issues that need to be resolved relating to the incorporation of users and carers at this level of planning. They include:

- Access: transport, venue, time, fees, expenses.

- Information: whether written or verbal, and how disseminated.

- Communication: avoidance of jargon. It is worth noting, however, that one user-carer group was so sensitive to staff's potential sense of threat that they learned the specialist language of the professionals (Goss and Miller, 1995).

- Power: who is the expert? Is it the user, the carer, the professional, or combinations of these?

- Group dynamics: agenda, background information, minutes, personalities, group cohesion.

INFORMATION

Introduction

174 Users and carers may have potent roles to play in gathering or interpreting information and opinion to inform service commissioners and the organisations that monitor service performance.

175 Good information is the lifeblood of effective commissioning and it comes in a variety of types and from a range of sources. Information ranges from the scientifically researched evidence-base through epidemiology and demographic data to more subjective data on individual needs which, when aggregated, may provide powerful evidence as to the way forward.

Strategic Planning and Needs Assessments

176 There are three broad types of information in respect of service development that are important elements in user and carer involvement. These are:

- information collected and provided for users and carers about the proposed and achieved responsiveness and comprehensiveness of local mental health services;

- information provided by users and carers about services they have used, know about, or would like;

- data collected within and between service systems, usually held on computer systems, about resources, demography, patient turnover, finances, workloads, contracts, patients' registers, care plans and similar. Users and carers may be particularly helpful to commissioners in interpreting data of this kind and, thereby, translating it into useful and relevant information.

177   A core difficulty for planners and commissioners is obtaining relevant information on the services that users and carers need. Systems related to the Patient's Charters and telephone information lines are available to inform users and carers about rights and services, but their uptake and utility is uncertain, and there is no central system for collecting evidence of outcome or unmet need. Similarly, Citizens Advice Bureaux and equivalent non-statutory agencies provide information directly to users and carers but, again, their processes and outcomes are rarely fed back into directing and planning statutory services.

178   Information on shortfalls in service provision may be acquired from users and carers who are involved in existing programmes and from individual reports. Collation of information from this rich vein by the responsible authorities could prove very helpful in focusing attention on gaps in services and would avoid accusations of tokenistic endeavours to engage users that may come when information presented by them is thought to have been ignored or stored.

Consumer Satisfaction and Complaints

179   This now leads to consideration of the roles of users and carers in supplying information to formal systems of complaint and through consumer satisfaction surveys.

180   Surveying service users and carers may be an evidential and systematic way of eliciting information on current service performance. In fact, consumer satisfaction and clinical audits of user opinion are now commonplace, but they do not necessarily answer questions about actual outcomes for users or carers. Much depends on the methods used and on the validity of the information to users and carers. A source of bias in the less vigorous surveys is the tendency for too many consumer satisfaction measures to flatter programmes.

181   In this approach to engaging users and carers, due thought should be given to the roles of a wider range of organisations outside the direct relationships between purchasers and providers. Users and carers and the staff of services should be aware that there are a variety of external mechanisms whereby users and carers may make powerful contributions to service monitoring and evaluation.

182   One such organisation is the Mental Health Act Commission (MHAC). Dialogue between the MHAC and users, when in its statutory role of listening to the complaints from detained patients, could be used more potently to affect service design. All too often, users experience the MHAC mechanisms as cumbersome and time-consuming, but this organisation has considerable volumes of information on user opinion that could be used in aggregated and anonymous forms to influence service directions more readily.

183 All of these mechanisms have their attractions and positive features, alongside certain limitations. Nonetheless, consumer audit seems a promising means of examining users' and carers' views on service programmes. This kind of information can be obtained via focus groups, by direct observation, and by appropriately reported home visits to users and carers.

184 Other, more ad hoc measures, may have their place, but they prevent comparison within and across services. What is needed is:

" ....*a systematic way of routinely establishing the outcome for the service user from their perspective* ...." (Huxley, 1996).

*The Involvement of
Users and Carers in
Planning Individual Care
Programmes and in
Delivering Services*

CHAPTER 11

INTRODUCTION

185 One of the HAS reviews (that on South Glamorgan) urged local service commissioners to move on developing a consumer strategy. It argued for the involvement of users and carers in purchasing processes.

186 In this field, models of care are central to the interests of users and carers. They wish to know if the models adopted in local services will result in the delivery of the items of service that they themselves value, alongside those that they are advised by professionals are in their interests.

187 As suggested earlier in this review, the involvement of users and carers in decisions which affect their lives is influenced significantly by different models of care (dependency versus equality) and the different definitions of need (agency versus client) that each model presupposes. What is not yet clear is how much user-informed or even user-led assessments of need (individual and population) have shifted medical or institutional models of disability towards social models. Current definitions of need continue to place emphasis on individual pathology and disability, rather than on models that combine these approaches with those that fully consider and respond to the social and systemic insufficiencies which perpetuate these factors.

188 Thus, there are differing levels in the delivery of services at which users and carers may be involved.

189 The contributors to the South Glamorgan review also recommended that tokenism be avoided by ensuring that users and carers contribute systematically to assessment, care planning, case management, after-care and staff training. These matters are provider responsibilities in the NHS and, for the most part, purchaser responsibilities in local authorities (as a result of the differing requirements on statutory services imposed by the *NHS and Community Care Act 1990*).

190 In similar terms, this review now moves from strategic issues to those more directly impacting on the delivery of services to individuals.

191 At the most practical level, users and carers are concerned about the package of services each will receive. The quality and extent of their involvement in their own case management is therefore a key issue.

CASE MANAGEMENT

192 Key elements in good case (and care) management relate to the nature, quality, comprehensiveness, liveliness and focus of individual assessments. Users and carers should be fully engaged in this process.

Assessment

193 Assessing individual need poses problems for staff of services, for users and for carers. Some may overvalue current ideologies of self-reliance, and thereby deny users their rights for proper dependency. Similarly, over-dependent or custodial provision can conflict with a user's wish for a service which facilitates autonomy. Professionals may also make Eurocentric assumptions about the nature of individuals' needs and how these are mediated by kinship support systems or religious or cultural customs.

194   It is clear from users' and carers' reports that staff of all disciplines – case managers, key workers, community psychiatric nurses, social workers, occupational therapists, psychiatrists, general practitioners, psychologists, support workers – require specialised assessment skills; information gathering is not enough. Assessment is a shared task, with a strong element of relationship-building between user and worker. Language and translation skills and cultural awareness should also be combined with other professional skills of engagement and interviewing style. Proper training in assessment is all too often lacking and it is alleged that as social administration (spot purchasing, brokerage, resource management and inspection) assumes greater importance in social services departments, assessment skills are declining.

195   The assessment of the needs of individuals and evaluation of service provision are closely linked. User opinion is becoming valued increasingly in the planning, monitoring and evaluation of mental health services. Incorporating a user dimension gives authenticity to the service, and integrity to the auditing process. This permits users' and carers' subjective views to be considered alongside more objective criteria, providing a more comprehensive critique of service provision. In turn, this can help to define and refine concepts of need and the assessment of need, with users and carers thereby contributing to more effective targeting of services.

196   Nonetheless, there is anecdotal evidence that users and carers are insufficiently informed about current assessment procedures. Summaries of assessment findings should be available to users and carers, at least in the form of a written care plan.

197   The assessment of the needs of carers is also not as prominent as most would wish. This process should become as routine as that of assessing the needs of users, especially so now that the relevant legislation is in place. The reasons are compelling. They are not related to the increasing demands of carers or to legal processes but are based on recognising that:

   •   increasingly, carers carry the burden of responsibility for supporting, monitoring and caring for users – therefore, there is a strong argument for a focus on sustaining them; and

   •   epidemiological studies indicate that the risks of individuals developing problems do cluster within groups of people who care for one another.

198   The ways in which users and carers can be more directly involved in assessment processes include their:

   •   sharing in more open dialogues with the professionals who assess their needs. This includes providing their views of the professionals themselves and not solely the material resources that they may deploy;

   •   devising assessment tools in conjunction with users and professional carers;

   •   having a key worker, advocate or equivalent worker present during assessment interviews, if required.

Planning and Monitoring Individual Care Programmes

199 An intention of the care programme approach (CPA) was that carers and users would become directly involved in assessment, care planning and review. There can be little doubt but that, after a slow start and patchy implementation, the CPA has become more rapidly adopted as a routine procedure used across England in the last two years. It has definitely fuelled the focused involvement of users in decisions on their own management and the involvement of carers in similar ways.

200 Nonetheless, there are challenges for users and for carers in contributing fully to care planning processes, including those of the CPA. These include the issues summarised here.

- At the individual level of planning, the greatest challenge is when users' and carers' interests diverge. When the frequency of this is not recognised in care planning processes, there is a risk of care plans focusing on users' needs, mainly if not exclusively. They may then fail or be unrealistic if assumptions are made about the capabilities and roles of carers.

- Soliciting information at the individual user level can be tokenistic, if service problems are ignored or unaffected by the opinions expressed.

- Communications at this level can be confounded by an excess of professional representation which can then distort their sense of group purpose or ownership, particularly if users and carers feel overfaced.

- Although the user-staff member interface is of key importance, good communication at this level is not necessarily replicated throughout agencies.

201 In circumstances of this nature, advocacy may become a central process at this planning level, and three kinds of advocacy may be applicable:

- **Clinical advocacy** – service staff working with users towards their preferred care or treatment outcomes.

- **Paid, independent advocacy** – such as that provided by a solicitor, welfare rights or legal adviser.

- **Self-advocacy** – in this circumstance, users act as their own advocates, collectively or individually, in negotiating the achievement of their own aims.

Users as Case and Care Managers

202 Currently, there appears to be little evidence nationally of users' involvement in direct case management, although carers in a very real sense often act, informally, as case managers. Indeed, under the CPA, a carer is sometimes the designated key worker for a user with enduring mental health needs. This contrasts with the situation in the United States of America where more and more users are taking on the roles of salaried case managers or mental health aides.

203 In one area of the UK (Sutton), a community care project partnered people with profound learning disabilities with people with mild learning disabilities, with a view to the latter acting as proxies or advocates. This compares with the buddying system used in the United States of America. Similar schemes exist in the UK and they may also act as models for involving mental health users. However, buddy schemes, while ensuring support for users via a personal and continuing relationship, often from a fellow user, do not generally offer paid posts, and professional roles and boundaries may be unclear. For instance, is a buddy a friend, an advocate, a case manager, a key worker or some other sort of professional or non-professional? What power does he or she have to secure better services for the user or the carer?

204 Another UK project with elderly mentally ill people (in Hereford and Worcester) sought to involve carers in assessment and care management. Apparently, carers in this area had felt too often dismissed by social workers and others as being over-involved with their respective users. A dialogue was opened between 10 social workers and 10 carers to focus on certain key issues relating to assessment and care management in order to ensure that consulting with users and carers becomes a matter of course rather than a special event.

205 For carers specifically, a recent development in South Wales has been the work of the PISCES multi-disciplinary team (Beck, Minghella and Ford, 1996), which was formed to address the needs of people caring for users of mental health services. Using a pragmatic, problem-solving approach, its broad aims are to educate carers about mental illness, to promote carers' social contacts, and to enhance the relationships between users and carers. The PISCES team complements rather than replaces existing services, and its remit includes providing support for key workers.

USERS AND CARERS AS SERVICE PROVIDERS

206 The experience of the HAS is that in many parts of England and Wales, key elements of service within the overall spectrum are provided by the independent sector. This sector includes the voluntary agencies within which users and carers may play significant roles.

207 Frequently, the HAS has found day centres, drop-in centres and occupational and recreational services playing vital roles by broadening the range, accessibility and comprehensiveness of local services. Very often, these services are valued highly by users and carers for their informality, responsiveness and availability. In this respect, users and carers can be said to be directly providing services. In some parts of the country, independent advocacy services are provided by users.

208 Nonetheless, the roles of these services are often seen as less than mainstream by the statutory sector. The risk of this is that their contributions may be eclipsed in the planning processes of health and local authorities and in those of trusts and other providers.

209   It is important that the value of these services is recognised and that they are enabled to assume a full role in the management processes that map the range of services provided across sectors and plan the development and sustain services for each locality. The intention should be to ensure recognition of valuable voluntary sector services within the descriptions of services provided and for their patterns of usage to be positively included when strategy and service operations are reviewed.

CHAPTER 12

The Involvement of Users and Carers in Evaluating and Managing Service Performance

INTRODUCTION

210 So far, this review has considered the roles that users and carers have been found to play and those that might be further developed in service commissioning, design and delivery. But these are not a full range of possible roles.

211 Each of the roles considered so far are directly related to the management of services generally and, as they develop, will make a growing contribution to aspects of performance management. In this chapter, the review considers other parts that users and carers play in the monitoring and evaluation of services and in quality promotion.

212 While the effects of recent legislation have yet to emerge, it is clear that government policies have achieved a great deal by way of identifying mental health as a key target for healthcare planning and delivery. Two ways in which changes in mental health and service provision can be tested are through:

- measures of treatment effectiveness or clinical outcome (on individuals or groups of users);

- service evaluation, including user and carer satisfaction measures (eg auditing, user feed-back, carer reports).

CLINICAL OUTCOMES AND EFFECTIVENESS

213 The government's commitment to improved overall mental health is exemplified in the Department of Health's funding of the Health of the Nation Outcome Scales (HONOS), which is a clinical measure of psychiatric and social morbidity to be used as a treatment baseline, and an instrument for establishing outcome and follow-up. It is expected to be used nationally in many mainstream settings. It is written in English, and therefore its sensitivity and appropriateness to ethnic groups whose primary language is not English has yet to be tested.

214 Treatment effectiveness is a narrow measure of change and does not necessarily reflect user satisfaction with treatment, nor does it shed light on the appropriateness of a service to users' needs. Indeed, these features may be on separate, though closely related, dimensions, linked, for instance, by compliance and ownership of care plans. Quality of life and consumer satisfaction measures are more suitable for this second set of outcome issues, but these need to be complemented by measures that are led by users and carers. Service issues such as appropriateness, accessibility and effectiveness can be addressed through user-led initiatives as well as through provider activity. Commissioners need the full story. However, there needs to be a suitably stable and supportive infrastructure of users, carers, professionals and managers to address and manage the challenges posed by gaining an appropriately broad range of outcome information.

215 One such problem, emerging increasingly as health services get to grips with CPA requirements, is the tension between users' and carers' roles. Can – and should – evaluative measures investigate user satisfaction with the carer's service? What if, as is so often the case, the carer is a parent or other close relative? Perhaps this is precisely the kind of close monitoring and questioning of relied-upon relationships, including those of worker-to-user and worker-to-carer, that services should evaluate.

QUALITY DEVELOPMENT AND SERVICE EVALUATION

216 For some non-mental health user groups, the Department of Health and the Social Services Inspectorate have invited carers to join advisory groups to develop their role as lay inspectors of residential homes that are regulated by social services departments. Perhaps mental health user groups could be mandated to propose members for training for equivalent duties in inspecting the range of statutory, private and independent sector provision in the mental health field.

217 Although relatively untested in the UK, some evidence from the United States of America suggests that users are likely to be more spontaneous in seeking and finding ways to elicit replies from respondents to enquiries about satisfaction with services. Users could become more involved in evaluation – ie in applying measures rather than in solely helping to devise them.

218 User involvement as a means of improving the quality of services does not generally include the objective of developing the quality of services provided for carers. Indeed, all too often, a common public assumption is that carers ill-treat users, whether through stress or malice, more frequently than is the case, when in fact the reverse is more often the case.

219 Service evaluation should be introduced at the point of entry to services, and should continue concurrently with users' and their carers' experiences of services. Retrospective evidence on a service at discharge or follow-up is less accurate and informative than assessing expectations at the outset, and afterwards evaluating satisfaction.

Conclusions

CHAPTER 13

The Way Forward

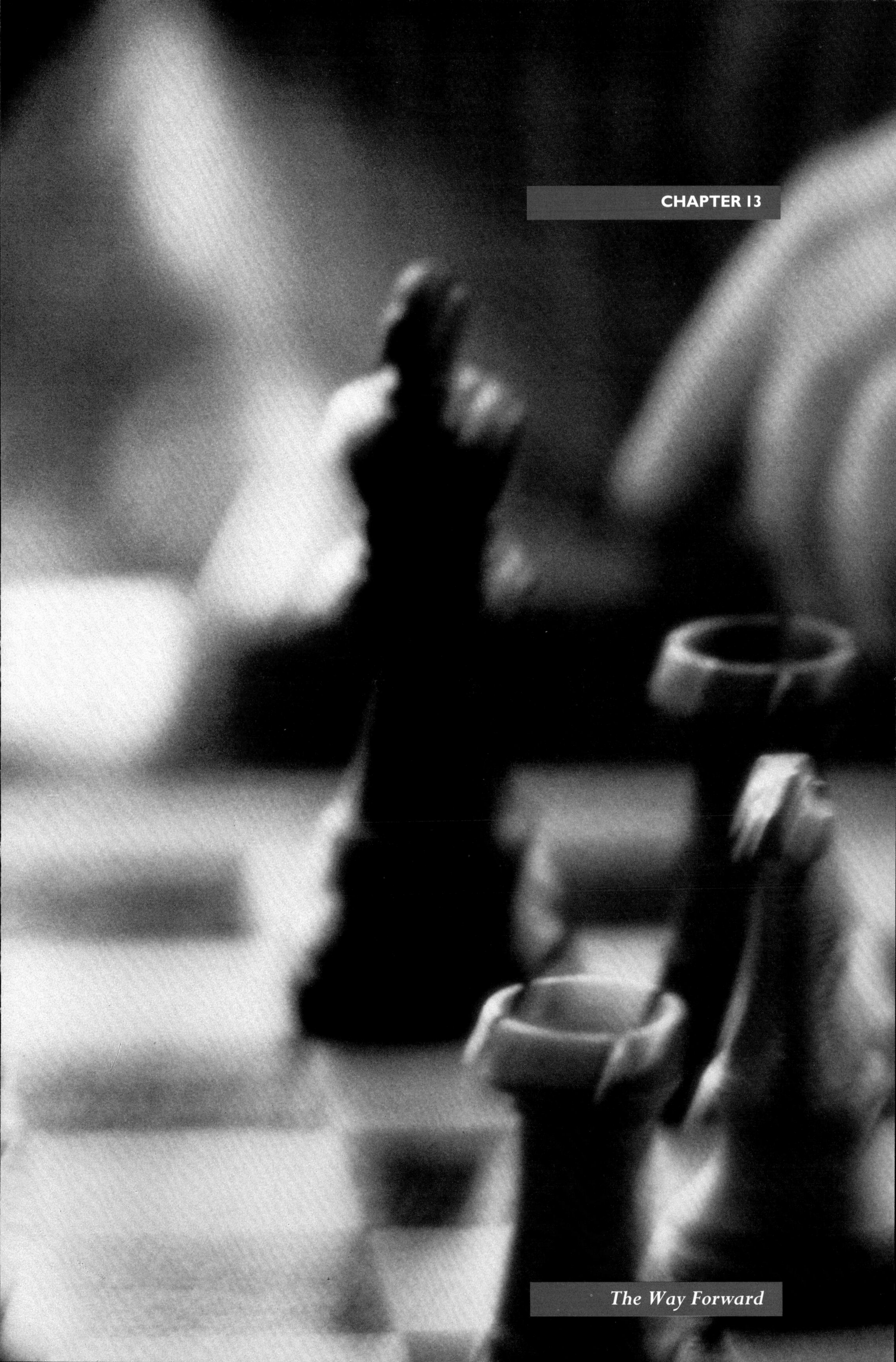

INTRODUCTION

220 Given the range of issues illustrated in this brief survey, there are a great many issues that could be considered further. The previous chapters summarise some of the key roles that users and carers may play. This report concentrates, perhaps inevitably given its origin, on developing further the active participation of users and carers at system, programme and individual levels in Huxley's typology. At a first pass, user and carer involvement may appear to relate to issues of consultation while in reality the span of activities covered by the word *involvement* is considerable. Each topic could be covered in further detail but this is beyond the scope of this brief review. Rather, previous chapters list some of the key factors that are considered likely to influence positive engagements between users and carers and the staff of mental health services as they currently stand. Each of these deserves further, separate study.

221 For the purposes of providing a way forward based on the account so far, this chapter highlights just two core matters: the possible development of professional advocacy and the training that advocates, and other user and carer representatives would need to fill expanding roles in service commissioning, planning and delivery systems. Finally, this review summarises some of the potential pitfalls perceived in current developments. Both of these areas will be controversial to some people.

ADVOCACY

222 Three broad types of advocacy were presented in chapter 11 – clinical, professional and self-advocacy. At national level, advocacy as political lobbying has directly and significantly contributed to new legislation, ie the *Carers (Recognition and Services) Act 1995*. At more local levels, eg Ashworth Hospital, independent professional advocacy has contributed to improved clinical services to patients, as well as to better practice by, and support, training and supervision for staff.

223 A further development of the advocate role could be the creation of the consultant advocate. Again, this development is considered earlier in this review in chapter 7. The consultant advocate could be a paid professional who specialises in representing and advancing the interests of carers and users. He or she would need a comprehensive understanding of mental disorder, service provision and management, planning and purchasing procedures and the legislation. Political know-how would be an advantage. The consultant advocate would operate independently of existing professional structures, but could link with a national network or representative council of consultant advocates. The consultant advocate could also supervise other advocates.

224 In terms of users or carers contributing to strategic planning, the consultant advocate could accompany users or carers to planning meetings, or substitute for either when a user or carer is unwell or unavailable.

225 Consultant advocates could be drawn from as wide a social range as users and carers. Many would be users or past users themselves, and they may be able to exert considerable influence, particularly if they are viewed as offering a professional service.

226 Becoming a consultant advocate would require training and accreditation, and this would need much thought and careful planning. But it would enable the consultant advocate to anticipate and avoid the many pitfalls that such a role might entail. Some stakeholders in services might be resistant to the idea of having user and carer representation in the planning process and, therefore, have an interest in seeing the establishment of consultant advocates not succeed. Support would have to be established from the outset of such an initiative. Detrimental attitudes could invalidate an initiative which is intrinsically precarious, because of the greater vulnerability of users and carers themselves, compared with other consumer representation groups.

TRAINING

227 There are three areas of training that seem especially relevant to user and carer involvement in commissioning, planning and delivering services. They are training:

- as care/service professionals;
- as strategic planners; and
- as operational managers.

These roles correspond roughly to the three levels of the typology shown earlier in Table 3 and summarised in Table 4.

Table 4

Training for Users and Carers	
Level	**Relevant Training Areas**
System Programme Individual	Strategic planning, business principles Management, information systems Service/care professional matters

228 Training of this kind would need a variety of inputs, as would the development of the consultant advocate. Training would also require funding, allocation of time and definition of curricula. Important goals of this kind cannot be achieved quickly or cheaply. Training is costly, and the cost is unlikely to be met adequately by one-off or short-term funding. Similarly, professionalism and experience cannot be hurried. A third input, often overlooked, is the provision of replacement carers or proxies for carers who have to leave dependent users in order to attend training courses, meetings, forums and similar.

PITFALLS

229 As well as the promises inherent in user and carer involvement in services, there are some dangers only touched upon thus far. One practical danger is the possible reduction or loss of state benefit to carers or users who may be receiving fees or expenses for their services as representatives or advocates, even though such funding may be a necessary and appropriate incentive or reward. Another is the impact of ambitious expectations of high-performing users or carers in contributing to strategic developments required of commissioning and planning bodies. Attempting too much too soon could be a recipe for early burnout.

230   Finally, there is the continuing question of how to achieve the best balance of user and carer representation on trust boards, in planning meetings and in the management of provider organisations. Opening this issue raises many more questions and challenges. Is the number of users and carers crucial, or are strength of personality and breadth of view more important? Is an advocate more, or less, likely to skew meetings or act on personal bias? Whatever the attendant risks, it is clear that users and carers must be brought much more to the forefront of mainstream mental health services. Not only does the new legislation require this, but services themselves will remain incomplete without it. Users, carers and the staff of services have a choice - to face the extending influence of users and carers as a threat or part of an adversarial process, or to take advantage of the opportunities provided by widening the pool of influence on service development by working together.

PART E

Bibliography, References and Annex

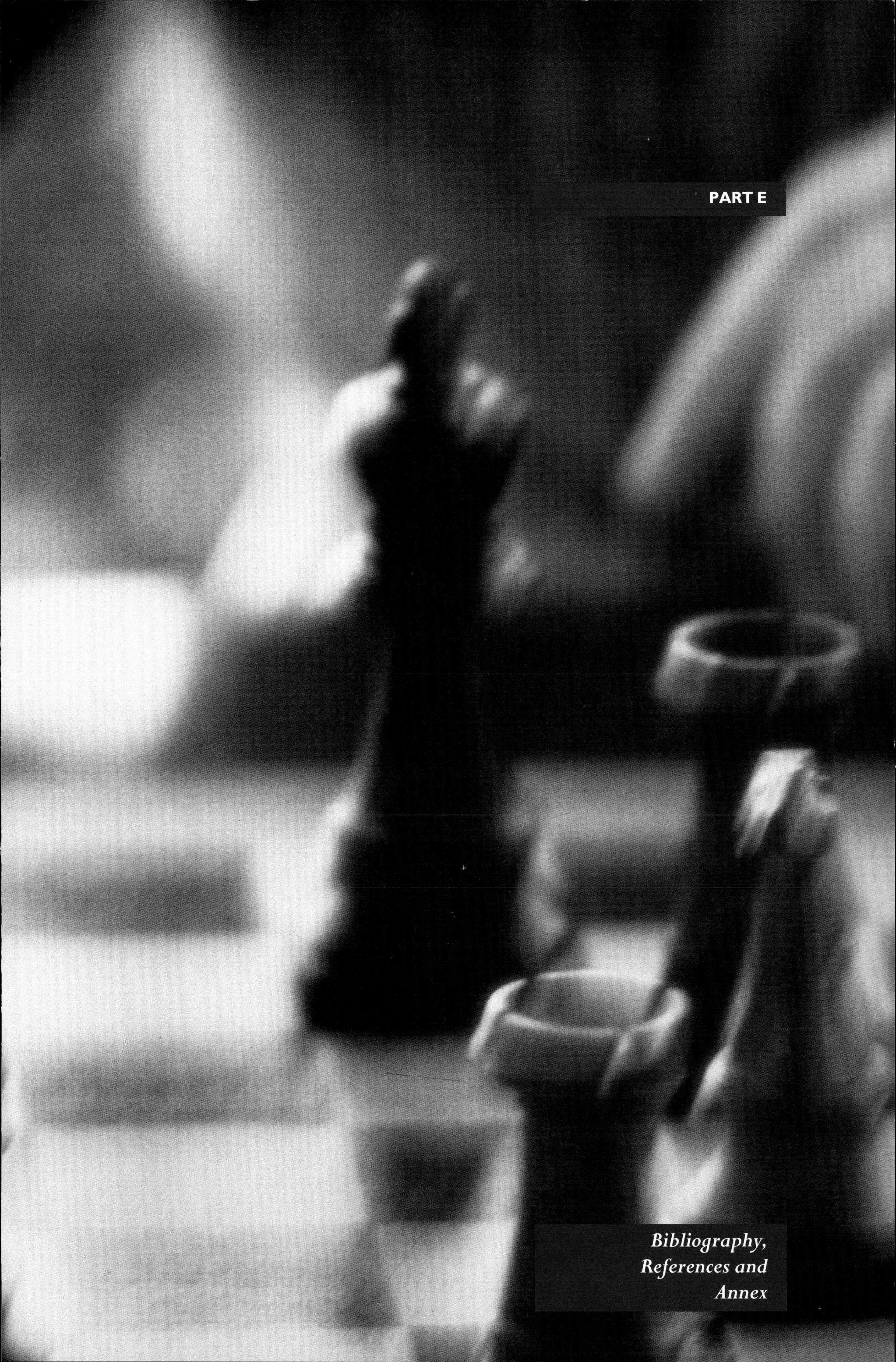

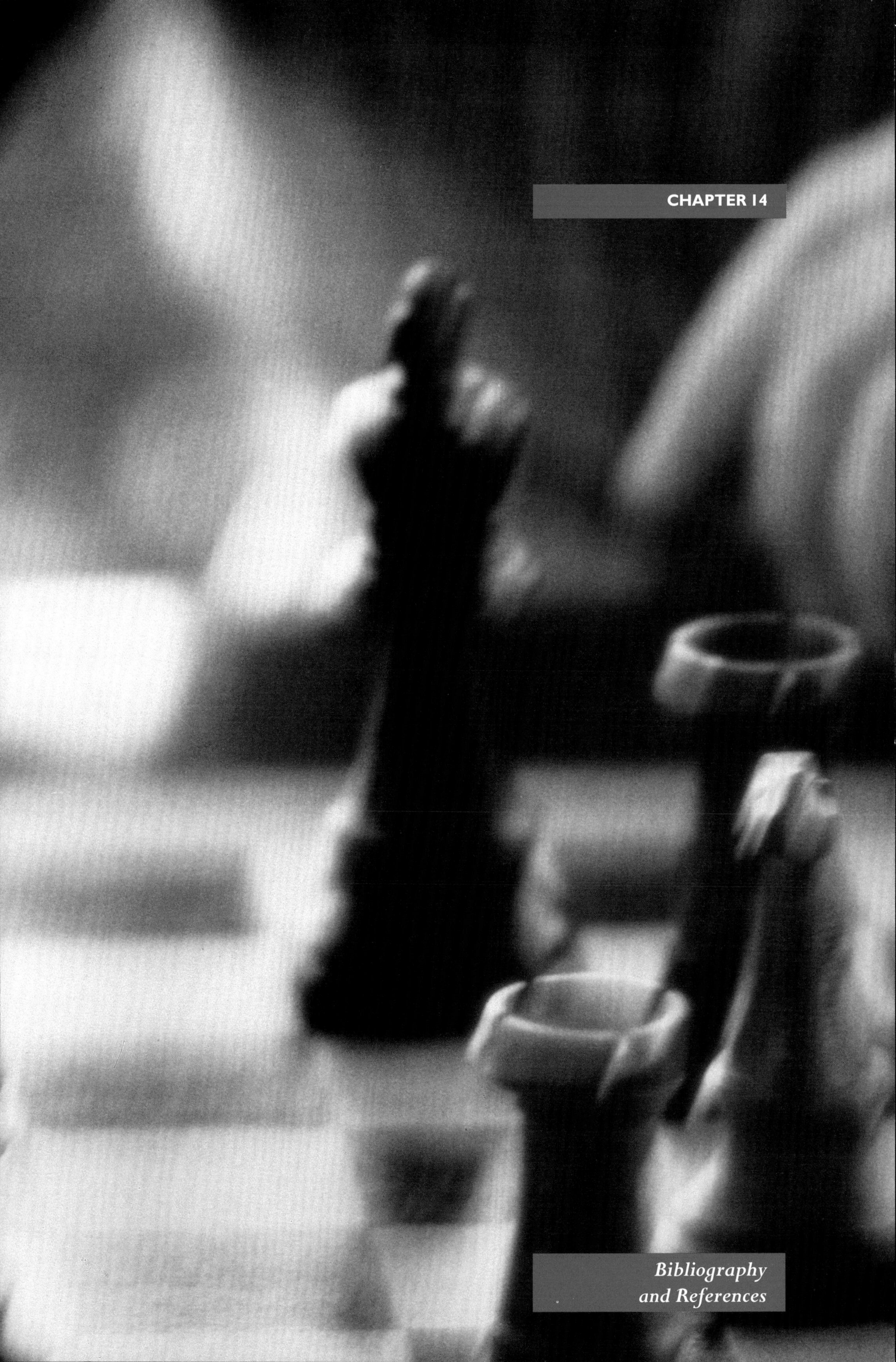

CHAPTER 14

Bibliography and References

MAJOR RELEVANT LEGISLATION AND GUIDANCE DOCUMENTS

National Assistance Act 1948. London, HMSO.

Health and Social Services and Social Security Adjudications Act 1983. London, HMSO.

Mental Health Act 1983. London, HMSO.

Claims and payments regulations 1987. Regulation 33. London, HMSO.

Griffiths R, (1988) *Community care: agenda for action: a report to the Secretary of State for Social Services.* London, HMSO.

Mental illness services : a strategy for Wales 1989. Cardiff, Welsh Office.

Department of Health, Department of Social Security, Welsh Office, Scottish Office Home and Health Department, (1989). *Caring for people: community care in the next decade and beyond.* London, HMSO, (Cm. 849).

The NHS and Community Care Act 1990. London, HMSO.

Department of Health, (1990). *Draft guidelines: Caring for people in the community, care in the next decade and beyond.* London, Department of Health.

Department of Health, (1991). *The patient's charter.* London, Department of Health.

Department of Health, (1992). *The health of the nation: a strategy for health in England.* London, HMSO, (Cm. 1986).

Mental Health Act Code of Practice (1993). London, HMSO.

NHS Management Executive, (1993). *Purchasing for health.* The Health Publications Unit.

Welsh Office and Welsh Health Planning Forum, (1993). *Protocol for investment in health gain – mental health.* Cardiff, Welsh Office.

Department of Health, (1994). *A framework for local community care charters in England.* London, Department of Health.

Carers (Recognition and Services) Act 1995. London, HMSO.

Department of Health, (1995). *Practical guidance on joint commissioning for project leaders.* London, Department of Health.

NHS Executive (1996). LASSL(96) 16/HSG(96)6. *An audit pack for the Care Programme Approach.* Department of Health.

BIBLIOGRAPHY

Ashworth CAB Patients Advocacy Service, Report (1995-1996). Special Hospitals Service Authority/Ashworth Hospital Authority.

Barnes M, Wistow G, (1994). *Learning to hear voices: listening to users of mental health services.* Journal of Mental Health, 3. 525-540.

Bates F, (1996). *Carers (Recognition and Services) Act, 1995: Guide for Practitioners.* Community Care.

Beck R, Minghella E, Ford R, (1996). *Talking it out.* Community Care, August/September.

BRIJ, (1996). *Mental health services for young people.* A report to the NHS Health Advisory Service (unpublished).

BRIJ, NHS Health Advisory Service, (1996). *Reports from review meetings in Nottingham.* BRIJ/NHS Health Advisory Service (unpublished).

Brunning H, Borley R, Poppleton W, Rogan J, (1994). *Local and vocal: how to involve service users in mental health.* Journal of Mental Health, 3, 119-122.

Carers National Association, (1995). *Carers National Association Information Pack.*

Drinkwater C, (1995). *Personal Communication.* In Together We Stand. NHS Health Advisory Service, 1995. London, HMSO.

Goss S, Miller C, (1995). *From margin to mainstream: developing user and carer centred community care.* Community Care/Joseph Rowntree Foundation.

Hoyes L, Lart R, Means R, Taylor M, (1995). *User empowerment and the reform of community care.* In: Lindow V, and Morris J, eds. Service User Involvement. Joseph Rowntree Foundation.

Huxley P, (1996). *Whose life is it anyway? Involving users and carers in the planning and delivery of mental health services.* Unpublished literature review written for the NHS Health Advisory Service.

Huxley P, Hoser B, (1996). *User involvement in mental health commissioning.* In: A Thematic Review of Commissioning Health Services for Mentally Ill People and of the Organisational Development Needs of Health Authorities with regard to this Client Group. A report to the NHS Health Advisory Service. (Unpublished).

Jansari R, (1993). *The carer's dilemma.* The Carer, March 1993, 8-9.

Kohner N, (1994). *A stronger voice.* The achievements of the carers' movement, 1963-1993. Carers National Association.

LeTouze S, (1993). *You can't just whistle....involving carers in consultation.* Carers National Association/Gatsby Charitable Foundation.

Lindow V, Morris J, (1995). *Service user involvement. Synthesis of findings and experience in the field of community care*. Joseph Rowntree Foundation.

Mental Health Users' Forum, Gwynedd (1995). *Annual report September 1994-August 1995*. Mental Health Users' Forum, Gwynedd.

Mental Health Users' Forum, (1996). *Report 1 April 1995-31 March 1996*. Mental Health Users' Forum, Gwynedd.

NHS Health Advisory Service, (1994). *A review of services for mentally ill people in the Gwynedd Health District*. The NHS Health Advisory Service and Social Services Inspectorate, Wales.

NHS Health Advisory Service, (1995a). *Together we stand. The commissioning, role and management of child and adolescent mental health services*. London, HMSO.

NHS Health Advisory Service, (1995b). *The substance of young needs. Commissioning and providing services for children and young people who use and misuse substances*. London, HMSO.

NHS Health Advisory Service, (1995c). *With care in mind secure. A review for the Special Hospitals Service Authority of the service provided by Ashworth Hospital*. London, Special Hospitals Service Authority.

NHS Health Advisory Service, (1995d). *A place in mind. Commissioning and providing mental health services for people who are homeless*. London, HMSO.

Rogers A, Pilgrim D, Lacey R, (1993). *Experiencing psychiatry: user's views of services*. Macmillan/MIND.

Warner N, (1994). *Community care: just a fairy tale? Report of a UK research survey commissioned by Carers National Association*. Carers National Association.

Warner N, (1995). *Better tomorrows: report of a national study of carers and the community care changes*. Carers National Association.

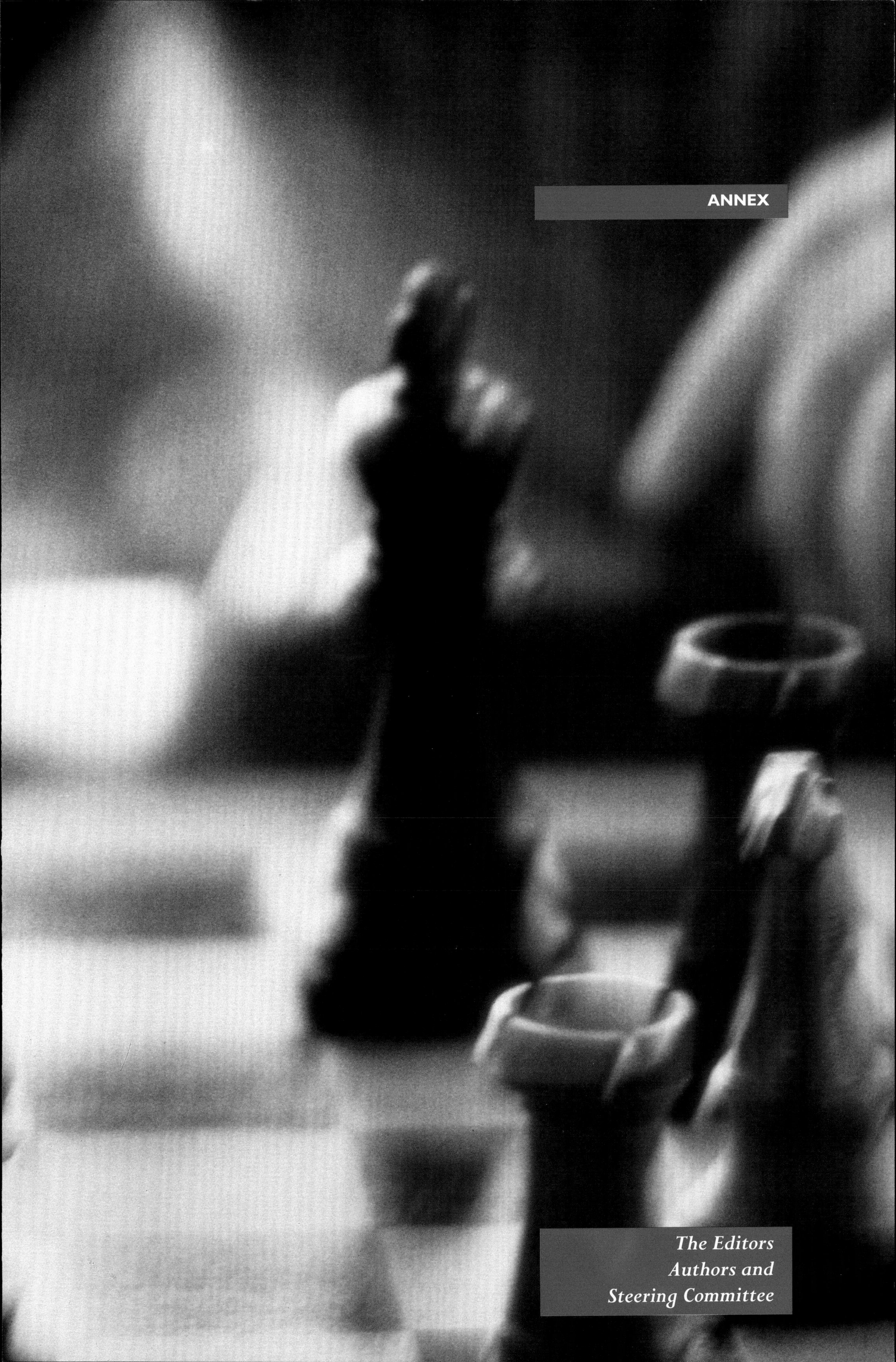

ANNEX

The Editors
Authors and
Steering Committee

THE EDITORS

Dr Richard Williams

Dr Richard Williams is the present Director of the NHS Health Advisory Service (HAS). Upon appointment in 1992, he was required to reposition the HAS so that it worked in accordance with the reformed health service. One of the new activities of the HAS, which he has developed, are the Thematic Reviews. Nine of these have been completed.

Richard Williams is also a Consultant Child and Adolescent Psychiatrist at the Bristol Royal Hospital for Sick Children, where he developed an extensive liaison and consultation service with other community childcare workers and the child health services. His particular clinical interests include the psychological impacts and treatment of life-threatening and chronic physical disorders and he has extensive experience of working with families who have experienced psychological trauma.

He has been involved in service management over a number of years and has a particular interest and experience in the theory and practice of leadership and the selection and development of leaders. Along with the Director of the Institute of Health Services Management, he inspired the creation of a Leadership Development Programme for Top Managers in Mental Health in 1994. Consequent on his work with the NHS, he has developed particular experience in the challenges posed to health authorities in purchasing comprehensive health services for mentally ill and elderly people.

Mrs Zena Muth

Mrs Zena Muth is the present Deputy Director of the NHS Health Advisory Service (HAS). She is a Department of Health civil servant and is responsible for the day-to-day management of the HAS. Since taking up appointment in 1993, she has held particular responsibility for the management and organisation of the NHS Drug Advisory Service, which is a component of the HAS. She has also undertaken a number of HAS visits and managed the team that conducted a review of Ashworth Special Hospital.

Mr Giles Emerson

Giles Emerson is a professional writer whose clients include most of the major government departments, as well as corporations in the private sector. He writes occasionally for *The Times* and *The Independent*, usually but not exclusively on the subject of the use and abuse of English, advocating a simple and direct approach. He has recently been commissioned to write a book on how to survive as a professional writer. Giles was educated at Exeter School in Devon and at Exeter College, Oxford, where he read English Language and Literature, graduating in 1978. He subsequently worked as a sub-editor on magazines about DIY, Gardening, War, and Sex among other subjects for Marshall Cavendish Partworks in London. In 1980, he joined the Central Office of Information as a writer and editor, where he gained much of his experience of writing for government organisations. In September 1984, Giles left the COI to learn more about the private sector and worked as a writer in a leading public relations company in Fleet Street for a year. In September 1985, he left London to set up his own business in Shropshire, where he works today.

THE AUTHORS

Mr Malcolm Firth

Malcolm Firth is a University Practice Teacher and Senior Psychiatric Social Worker in central Manchester, and works mainly with adults who have severe and enduring mental disorders. He is also Clinical Director of Mental Health Social Work in Primary Care, managing two innovative projects. He has published several articles on specialist social work practice and on practice learning. His research interests include needs assessment, psychotherapy training, and the primary-secondary care interface.

Professor Michael Kerfoot

Professor Michael Kerfoot is the recently-appointed Professor of Child and Adolescent Policy and Research in the School of Psychiatry and Behavioural Sciences, University of Manchester. He is also Co-director of the Mental Health Social Work Research and Staff Development Unit. He has 16 years experience of working as a practitioner in child and adolescent mental health services in Liverpool, Newcastle and Manchester. His main research interest has been in adolescent suicidal behaviour, but he has also conducted research into psychiatric emergencies, and into joint commissioning of services. He is currently undertaking a major evaluative study of brief intervention with suicidal adolescents and their families. Twice, he has been a visiting Research Associate at the Los Angeles Suicide Prevention Centre, and is an Honorary Consultant to The Samaritans.

THE STEERING COMMITTEE

Mr Brian Hoser

Brian Hoser is a director of the BRIJ CST, a project primarily involved in developing employment opportunities for individuals with long-term mental health problems. He has worked in the field of user involvement in mental health for the past 10 years with health authorities, social services departments, housing agencies, voluntary organisations and service user and carer groups. He has been a mental health service user for 11 years.

He has been involved in several publications concerned mainly with improving mental health services through user and carer involvement, advocacy groups and mental health services for homeless people.

Professor Peter Huxley

Peter Huxley is Professor of Psychiatric Social Work and Head of the School of Psychiatry and Behavioural Sciences at the University of Manchester. He is the author of six books (including Mental Illness in the Community (Tavistock, 1980); Common Mental Disorder: A Biosocial Model (Routledge, 1992); and Quality of Life and Mental Health Services (Routledge, 1996)) and numerous articles on psychiatric social work and social psychiatry. He has conducted research into the efficacy of community mental health services and the quality of life of people with severe mental illness in the UK and in the United States of America at the County Mental Health Center, Boulder, Colorado.

Mr Ravindra Jansari

Ravindra Jansari worked as a television engineer for many years before giving up work to look after his elderly invalid parents.

As a full-time carer, he has campaigned on behalf of carers through the Carers National Association and published articles and given radio interviews and talks highlighting the problems of carers and users.

Ravindra is a member of the NHS Health Advisory Service Advisory Panel and is actively involved in several carers organisations as a committee member.

Ms Jill Pitkeathley

Jill Pitkeathley trained as a social worker and worked as a child care officer, then as a voluntary services co-ordinator for West Berkshire Health Authority. She became Director of the National Council for Carers and their Elderly Dependants in 1986. Following the merger with the Association of Carers, she became the first Director of the Carers National Association in 1988. From small beginnings, the Association has grown in size and influence and now has 80 staff, 120 branches and a structure which covers the whole of the UK. It is seen as the main organisation campaigning for a fairer deal for carers.

Jill Pitkeathley was a member of the advisory group to the Griffiths Review of Community Care and is a current member of the NHS Health Advisory Service Advisory Panel and of the Board of Governors of the National Institute of Social Work.

Ms Louise Reynolds

Louise Reynolds is a founder member, and is currently company secretary, of the North Wales Mental Health Users Forum and Vice Chair of the Mental Health Advocacy Scheme. She has been active in encouraging the involvement of users in the former county of Gwynedd, was the first user representative in the county and now works at local, county and North Wales levels. Before becoming a mental health service user in 1990, she gained a science degree at the University of Bristol and worked as a computer programmer and also as a Scientific Officer at the Transport and Road Research Laboratory. She is currently studying for a Diploma in Health and Social Welfare. She has a special interest in training users and service providers in issues around user involvement and in finding ways of making user involvement meaningful. She is a member of the NHS Health Advisory Service Advisory Panel.

Mr Edward Unsworth

Ted Unsworth is Director of Social Services for Cambridgeshire where he has worked in a variety of different roles since 1976 following earlier service with Cheshire and North Yorkshire Social Services Departments. He was active in helping to create the British Association of Social Workers and throughout has retained an interest in the professional development of social care services, for instance by acting as an external assessor to qualifying training courses approved by the Central Council for Education and Training in Social Work.

He entered the service as a mental health social work practitioner and has maintained an interest in this sector of service throughout his career. Currently, his expertise is sought on a range of issues including strengthening links between local government and the NHS and with services for mentally disordered offenders and for people who misuse alcohol and drugs. He is a member of the Association of Directors of Social Services Mental Health Strategy Group, the NHS Health Advisory Service Advisory Panel and chairman of the Cambridgeshire Drug Action Team.